Biology for
High School

Biology for High School

First Edition, 2019

Copyright @ Elemental Science, Inc.

Email: support@elementalscience.com

ISBN #978-1-935614-67-8

Printed in the USA for worldwide distribution

For more copies write to:
Elemental Science
PO Box 79
Niceville, FL 32588
support@elementalscience.com

Copyright Policy

Biology for High School Table of Contents

Introduction

Unit 1: Cell Structure, Function, and Reproduction

Unit 2: Genetics and Evolution

Unit 3: Ecology, Eukaryotes, and Plant Life

Unit 4: Animals and the Human Body

Appendix

Introduction to this Guide

Welcome to Biology! This year, you will learn about biochemistry, cell structure, photosynthesis, genetics, plants, microorganisms, anatomy, and much more. In this guide, you will find three types of schedules, as well as notes with the assignments for each week. To get links to the textbook, teacher guide, experiment, and quick-links for the activities in this guide, please visit:

🖥 https://elementalscience.com/blogs/resources/bhs

Three Courses in One

This guide contains the plans for three courses in one book. These are:

☞ **Honors** - The plans in this option are for a lab science, 1-credit *Honors Biology* course. There are textbook assignments, experiments, events in science, optional hands-on activities, and written work with these plans. Expect to take about 5 to 6 hours a week to complete these plans. We recommend this option for students who plan on going into the sciences. The honors course will also fulfill a lab science credit for graduation.

☞ **Standard** - The plans in this option are for a standard lab science, 1-credit *High School Biology* course. There are textbook assignments, experiments, and written work with these plans. Expect to take about 4 to 5 hours a week to complete these plans. We recommend this option for students who are not and for students who are planning on going into the sciences. The standard course will fulfill a lab science credit for graduation.

☞ **Survey** - The plans in this option are for an information-only, 1-credit *Survey of Biology* course. There are textbook assignments, written work, and events in science with these plans. There are no experiments or hands-on activities scheduled with these plans. Expect to take about 4 to 5 hours a week to complete these plans. We recommend this option for students who are not planning on going into the sciences and do not need a lab science credit for graduation.

Each of the scheduling pages will note at the top which course the plans are for. These schedules for these courses are suggestions; please check with your local oversight contact to make sure that you are meeting your state's graduation requirements. Please feel free to tailor this program to the needs of your students.

An Explanation of the Sections

After the scheduling pages, you will find the notes sheets. These sheets are divided into four sections - textbook, experiments, events in science, and hands-on activities. Here is an explanation of each of these sections.

Textbook

For this study, we have chosen to use a widely available, standard text book, *CK-12 Biology*.

You can download this text as a pdf from the resource page above. You will complete the reading assignment and then answer several of the questions from the text. These answers should be added to the reading section of the science notebooks. You will also define several of the key terms from the chapter. The definitions should be added to the glossary section of the science notebook.

Experiment

All the experiments come from *Illustrated Guide to Home Biology Experiments*, along with the corresponding experiment kit. You can download the guide for free and purchase the kit (BK01A Standard/Honors Home School Biology Laboratory Kit) from here:

🖥 https://www.thehomescientist.com/bk01-main.php

With each of these experiments, you will find a purpose, required pre-reading, procedure, lab notebook assignments, and lab questions. For each week, we have included a supply list for your convenience. If you would like to see a full list of the household supplies you will need in addition to the experiment kit, please see pg. 239 in the Appendix.

We have also incorporated an optional online lab into the standard course. These online labs are available through Beyond Labz. You can visit the resource page for this program for directions on how to sign up and use these labs or visit their website directly at:

🖥 https://www.beyondlabz.com/

As part of unit four, the standard- and honors-course students will complete a full lab report for one of the experiments. We have included an explanation of what a full lab report includes after this introduction.

Events in Science

This section gives two options for the Events in Science section. One will familiarize you with current events in science, as you research on the internet for the various topics. The other will familiarize you with the key historical figures in biology through the scientist biography report. We have included two articles to explain these options in more depth following this introduction.

Hands-on Activities

We have also included optional hands-on experiments for each week. You can see a list of the supplies you will need for these in the Appendix on pg. 242.

The Science Notebook

This year, you will each create a science notebook. Each notebook should contain the following sections:

📖 Reading (All Students) - This section of the notebook will contain any notes you have taken, along with the answers to the questions that were assigned each week.

📖 Lab (Standard- and Honors-Course Students Only) - This section of the notebook will house the notes from the experiments you have done, along with any other materials relating to the labs.

📖 Events (Survey- and Honors-Course Students Only) - This section of the notebook will include either the current events article summaries or the historical reports you have done.

📖 Glossary (All Students) - This section of the notebook will have the definitions for the assigned vocabulary words.

This notebook can be a composition book, divided into the required sections, or a three-ring binder with dividers for each section.

Grading and Credits

The three options in this guide meet the requirements for a full credit of high school biology, as explained above. Each week, the student will answer lab and textbook questions, do events in science written work, and define vocabulary that can count toward a classwork grade for the course. The textbook for this course has chapter tests available for free in the quizzes and tests packet. We suggest that you use these for the exam grade for the course. We suggest you use the following percentages to come up with a final grade for the course:

☞ Class work: 70%
☞ Exam: 30%

Note - A grading rubric for the Scientist Biography Reports can be found on pg. 244 in the Appendix.

Students Going Into The Sciences

If your students plan to go on to major in the sciences, we suggest that you also add an in-depth project and a research report at some point during the year to this program. An explanation of the in-depth project and of the research report can be found on the following pages.

Final Thoughts

As the authors and publishers of this curriculum, we encourage you to contact us with any questions or problems that you might have concerning *Biology for High School* at support@ elementalscience.com. We will be more than happy to answer you as soon as we are able. We trust that you and your students will enjoy *Biology for High School*!

What a full Lab Report should include

It is very important that all students begin to understand the process of writing scientific laboratory reports. Learning technical writing is a skill that must be practiced in order to become proficient. Having your students write laboratory reports also helps them to think critically as they analyzes the data that they have observed in the experiments. It will also give them a good basis for scientific writing that will help to prepare them for college level work.

The Components

Although there are some variations to a scientific lab report depending on the discipline you are writing for, they all contain the same basic components. Below is a general outline of the components of a scientific lab report:

1. Title
2. Abstract
3. Introduction
4. Materials and Procedure
5. Results (includes observations and data)
6. Conclusion
7. Works Cited

Each section of the scientific lab report should include specific information. The following is an explanation of what each section should have.

Title

This section should summarize the scientific experiment in 10 words or less and use key words in the report.

Abstract

An abstract gives a one paragraph synopsis of the research that the scientist has done. Generally, the scientist will write a full research report and the abstract can let the reader know if reading the full report would be beneficial. The abstract should contain the data and conclusions of the report in two hundred words or less. If you have not completed an associated research report, you can use this to summarize their research.

Introduction

The introduction section of the report is designed to give the reader the basis for the report, the reason why it was completed, and the background about what is already known about the experiment. Usually this section answers, "Why did we do this study?", "What information was known before we began the experiment?", and "What is the purpose of the study?"

Materials and Procedures

This section tells the reader what specific equipment and supplies were used in the experiment. You will also need to describe how the equipment and supplies were used. It is also important to describe when and where the experiment was conducted. The purpose of this information is to allow any person that reads the scientific report to be able to replicate the results. Without being able to replicate the results, the data obtained are not confirmable.

Results

The main purpose of the results section is to present the data that were obtained during the experiment. It is important that you present just the data and avoid analyzing or making conclusions about the data, as there is another section for this. The results section is also the place to include tables, graphs, and data tables. These should be easily understood by the average reader and be well labeled.

Conclusion

In the conclusion section you should focus on analyzing the data. Don't just reiterate the data; rather, draw conclusions from the data. It is permissible to draw speculative conclusions; just remember to state that is what you are doing. In this section, you should also discuss if the hypothesis was confirmed or invalidated and if further experimentation should be carried out to refine your hypothesis. You must also discuss any errors that occurred during the lab; these are usually not human errors but rather systematic errors that occur while conducting the experiment. Systematic errors can be caused by improper calibration of equipment, changes in the environment, and estimation errors. In the conclusion, it is important to present these errors that may have occurred in your experiment. This section is usually written in third person, passive, past tense.

Works Cited

This is the listing of the research materials used in the report to give background or to help corroborate the data. All outside sources must be cited. The format you will use for the works cited (i.e., MLA, APA, Turabian etc.) will depend upon the scientific field that this lab report relates to.

The Style

When formatting the lab reports, there are some basic guidelines about style that you should know.

1. Have a one inch margin and use 12pt New Times Roman font.

2. All chemical formulas should be formatted properly (i.e. Cl_2, H_2O)

3. Chemical structures that are drawn should be neat and easily readable.

4. Pay attention to formatting, spelling, and the overall look of the lab report.

More Information on Lab Reports

We recommend two books for your student to better prepare for writing scientific papers and lab reports. These books cover in greater detail what we covered in the previous section and they can be easily obtained from Amazon or your university library.

&✓ *A Student Handbook For Writing In Biology* by Karin Kinsely

&✓ *Making Sense: Life Sciences: A Student's Guide to Research and Writing* by Margot Northey

Adding Current Events into your Science Studies

Step 1 - Choose the article.

The first step is to choose an appropriate article. Usually, I try to pick one from the field of science that we are studying. You can subscribe to a kid's science magazine, do a Google search, or check out our Science News for Students to find possible articles. Once you have collected a list of options, peruse through them and pick one that you think will interest your student.

Step 2 - Read the article.

The next step is to have the students read the actual article. Simply hand them the article and tell each of them to come see you when they are done reading it.

Step 3 - Discuss the article.

The third step is to discuss the article the student is reading. I typically ask questions like:

- What was the article about?
- What do you think about (a piece of research or an experiment that the article pointed out)?
- How does the article relate to (something that we have studied on the subject)?
- Did you find the article to be interesting?
- Do you agree with the opinion(s) stated in the article?

Step 4 - Write a summary.

The final step to adding current events to your science students is to have each student write a summary. Once you finish the discussion, ask your students to write three to five sentences on the article, including their opinion on it. Since you have already talked about the piece, this step is easy for the students to do.

The Scientist Biography Report

Step 1 - Research

Begin by looking for a biography on the scientist at the library. Then, look for articles on the chemist in magazines, newspapers, encyclopedias, or on the Internet. You will need to know the following about your scientist to write your report:

📕 Biographical information on the scientist (i.e., where they were born, their parents, siblings, and how they grew up);

📕 The scientist's education (i.e., where they went to school, what kind of student they were, what they studied, and so on);

📕 Their scientific contributions (i.e., research that they participated in, any significant discoveries they made, and the state of the world at the time of their contributions).

As you read over the material you have gathered, be sure to write down any facts you glean in your own words. You can do this on the sheet below or on separate index cards. You can read more about this method by clicking below:

💻 http://elementalblogging.com/the-index-card-system/

Step 2 - Create an Outline

Now that your research is completed, you are ready to begin the process of writing a report on your chosen scientist. You are going to organize the notes you took during step two into a formal outline, which you will use next week to write the rough draft of your report. Use the outline template provided on the student sheets as a guide. You should include information on why you chose the particular scientist in your introduction section. For the conclusion section of the outline, you need to include why you believe someone else should learn about your chosen scientist and your impression of the scientist (i.e., Did you like the scientist? Do you feel that they made a significant impact on the field of chemistry?).

The outline you create can look like the one below:

Scientist Biography Outline

I. Introduction & Biological Information on the Scientist (4-6 points)

II. The Scientist's Education (4-6 points)

III. The Scientist's Contributions (1-3 sub categories each with 4-5 points)

IV. Conclusion (4-5 points)

Step 3 - Write a Rough Draft

In the last step, you created a formal outline for your scientist biography report; now, it is time to take that outline and turn it into a rough draft. Simply take the points on your outline, combine them, and add in sentence openers to create a cohesive paragraph. Here's what your rough draft should look like:

- 📖 Paragraph 1 (from outline point I): introduce the scientist;
- 📖 Paragraph 2 (from outline point II): tell about the scientist's education;
- 📖 Paragraph 3-5 (from outline point III): share the scientist's contributions (one paragraph for each contribution);
- 📖 Paragraph 6 (from outline point IV): share your thoughts on the scientist and why someone should learn about him or her.

You can choose to hand write or type up your rough draft on a separate sheet of paper. However, keep in mind that you will need a typed version for the final step.

Step 5- Revise to Create a Final Draft

Now that you have a typed, double-spaced rough draft, look over it one more time to make any changes you would like. Then, have your teacher or one of your peers look over the paper for you to correct any errors and bring clarity to any of the unclear sections. Once this is complete, make the necessary changes to your paper to create your final draft.

The In-depth Project

For the in-depth project, the student will follow the same steps as they did in the science fair project. However, during the high school years, they will go deeper with each step. For example, in middle school, they may have had only five references, whereas in high school, they will need around fifteen to twenty references for their research. The in-depth project should also be a semester long process, rather than several weeks.

So, let's say the student chooses to do an in-depth project involving hydroponics. They want to know if the use of hydroponics will increase plant yield. Their hypothesis, which is supported by their research, states that "Hydroponics produces a superior yield compared to traditional growing methods." For their experiment, they set up two growing environments—one in potting soil and one using hydroponics. At the middle school level, the students would have only used one type of plant observed over two to three weeks. Now, for the in-depth project, they will use multiple types of plants, such as a flower, a grass, a lettuce, and a vegetable, which they allow to grow for two to three months. The students will still need to record their observations and data daily.

Once their experiment is completed, the students will use their mathematical knowledge to analyze and report their findings. Their conclusions will be much more in depth and will include their own inferences about the findings. Once their project is complete, the student should each give a ten to fifteen minute oral presentation explaining their projects and their results.

More Information

For more information on how to do a science fair project, please read the following:

- ᧖ *The Science Fair Project: A Step-by-Step Guide* by Brad and Paige Hudson
- ᧖ The Science Fair Project Session: https://elementalscience.com/blogs/news/science-fair

The Research Report

The research report process should take the students about half the year to complete. Begin by having every student pick a topic and research the topic, finding out as much material as they can. They can look in biological abstracts, Google Scholar, reference books, and encyclopedias. As they find information, have them take notes that are separated into subtopics. We recommend that they put the different pieces of information on index cards that are numbered for each reference and subtopic. However, if you want the students to use a computer program rather than hand–written notes, we recommend RefWorks, which is widely used as a reference software in colleges today.

The next step is to have the students write their thesis statements. The purpose of the thesis statement is to give a focus to the paper. Their statements should give their point of view or slant on the topic. You can ask them the following questions to help them craft a thesis statement:

- What do you know currently about the topic?
- What are questions that you have about the topic?
- How do you feel about the topic?

This is a fluid process, so their thesis statements may need to be revised several times before the first draft is written.

After the students have written their thesis statements, they each needs to create an outline for their papers from the information that they gathered. Their papers needs to have three sections:

1. **Introduction** – This section gives a brief look at the topic, states their thesis statement, and explains why they choose the topic.
2. **Body** – This is the main part of their paper and contains multiple paragraphs full of information that supports the thesis statement. The body should include several quotes from experts or excerpts from their research that give credence to the thesis statement about the topic.
3. **Conclusion** – This section will restate the thesis statement, summarize the supporting information, and apply it to today.

After you have approved their outline, have each student turn in a rough draft of the paper. If they are not familiar with writing research papers, you may want to have them turn in multiple drafts. Either way, the final research report should be six to eight pages in length (double-spaced). You are looking to make sure that the paper is written in the third person, that it uses the correct MLA style documentation, and that the paper has a strong thesis statement with good supporting evidence.

Biology for High School

Unit 1 - Cell Structure, Function, and Reproduction

Week 1 Notes - Introduction to Biology

Textbook Assignments
Reading
 📖 *CK-12 Biology* Sections 1.1, 1.2
Written
 After you finish reading, answer questions #1-6 in section 1.2 and file your work in the reading section of your science notebook. Then, define the following terms in the glossary section of your science notebook:

- ☐ Dependent variable
- ☐ Independent variable
- ☐ Scientific theory
- ☐ Scientific law
- ☐ Stage
- ☐ Turret
- ☐ Aperture
- ☐ Rheostat

Experiment - Using a Microscope
Purpose
 The purpose of this lab is to familiarize you with how biology labs work and to get you comfortable with using the *Illustrated Guide to Home Biology Experiments*.
Pre-Reading
 ↫ Read the background and procedure sections for the "Using the Microscope" lab on pg. 53 in the *Illustrated Guide to Home Biology Experiments*.
Procedure
 ✓ Do the lab entitled "Using the Microscope" lab on pg. 53 in the *Illustrated Guide to Home Biology Experiments*.
Lab Notebook
 ☞ Write down on a sheet of paper or type out your notes as you do the experiment. After you are done, print out your lab notes and add them to the lab section of your science notebook. (*See pp. 4-6 in the Illustrated Guide to Home Biology Experiments for information about a lab notebook.*)
Lab Review Questions
 🖎 Complete the review questions of the "Using the Microscope" lab on pg. 61 in the *Illustrated Guide to Home Biology Experiments*. Record the answers in the lab section of your science notebook.

Online Lab
 ☞ There is no online lab scheduled for this week.

Events in Science

Current Events

⊕ Find a current events article relating to the field of biochemistry and complete the article summary sheet found on pg. 246 of the Appendix. Once you are done, add the sheet to the events section of your science notebook.

Historical Figures

⊕ Begin to research the life and work of Aristotle, who is considered by many to be the father of biology. You will have three weeks to complete your research. After that, you will have two weeks to prepare a two to three page paper on this scientist and his contributions to the field of biology.

Hands-on Activity

Optional Hands-on

✂ Practice using a microscope by making wet mount and dry mount slides. Directions can be found here: https://elementalscience.com/blogs/science-activities/how-to-make-a-microscope-slide.

Week 1 Supply List

Weekly Experiment	
Supplies from BK01A Biology Kit	☐ Goggles, Forceps, Ruler (millimeter scale)
Additional Supplies From Home	☐ Gloves, Lamp or book light, Microscope, Scissors, Slide - prepared (bacteria or diatoms), Notebook or copy paper
Hands-on Activity	
Supplies Needed	☐ Microscope, Blank slides, Various materials to examine

Week 1	Unit 1 (Honors Course)			5-Day
Weekly Topic				

→ This week will be an introduction to biology.

	Day 1	Day 2	Day 3	Day 4	Day 5
Textbook and Experiment	❑ Read *CK-12 Biology* Section 1.1.	❑ Read *CK-12 Biology* Section 1.2.	❑ Read the background and procedure sections for the week's lab.	❑ Do the "Using a Microscope" lab on pg. 53 in *Illustrated Guide to Home Biology Experiments*.	❑ Do the optional Hands-on Assignment - Wet and Dry Mount Slides.
Writing	❑ Add the vocabulary to the glossary section of your science notebook.	❑ Answer the assigned questions in the reading section of your science notebook.		❑ Record what you have done in the lab section of your science notebook.	❑ Complete the lab review questions for the week.
Events in Science	❑ Choose one of the Events in Science assignments to do and add your work to the events section of your science notebook.				

Other Notes

Week 1	Unit 1 (Standard Course)		4-Day

Weekly Topic

→ This week will be an introduction to biology.

	Day 1	Day 2	Day 3	Day 4
Textbook and Experiment	☐ Read *CK-12 Biology* Section 1.1.	☐ Read *CK-12 Biology* Section 1.2.	☐ Read the background and procedure sections for the week's lab.	☐ Do the "Using a Microscope" lab on pg. 53 in *Illustrated Guide to Home Biology Experiments*.
Writing	☐ Add the vocabulary to the glossary section of your science notebook.	☐ Answer the assigned questions in the reading section of your science notebook.		☐ Record what you have done in the lab section of your science notebook.

Other Notes

Week 1	Unit 1 (Survey Course)	2-Day

Weekly Topic

→ This week will be an introduction to biology.

	Day 1	Day 2
Textbook	❏ Read *CK-12 Biology* Section 1.1.	❏ Read *CK-12 Biology* Section 1.2.
Writing	❏ Add the vocabulary to the glossary section of your science notebook.	❏ Answer the assigned questions in the reading section of your science notebook.
Events in Science	❏ Choose one of the Events in Science assignments to do and add your work to the events section of your science notebook.	

Other Notes

Week 2 Notes - Chemistry of Life, part 1

Textbook Assignments
Reading
📖 *CK-12 Biology* Sections 2.1, 2.2

Written
After you finish reading, answer questions #1-7 in section 2.1 and file your work in the reading section of your science notebook. Then, define the following terms in the glossary section of your science notebook:

- Amino Acid
- Carbohydrate
- Complementary Base Pair
- DNA
- Lipid
- Monosaccharide
- Polysaccharide
- RNA
- Anabolic Reaction
- Catabolic Reaction

Experiment - Mounting Specimens
Purpose
The purpose of this lab is to familiarize you with how to mount specimens.

Pre-Reading
↝ Read the background and procedure sections for the "Mounting Specimens" lab on pg. 63 in the *Illustrated Guide to Home Biology Experiments*.

Procedure
✓ Do the lab entitled "Mounting Specimens" on pg. 63 in the *Illustrated Guide to Home Biology Experiments*.

Lab Notebook
☞ Write down on a sheet of paper or type out your notes as you do the experiment. After you are done, print out your lab notes and add them to the lab section of your science notebook.

Lab Review Questions
🍂 Complete the review questions of the "Mounting Specimens" lab on pg. 69 in the *Illustrated Guide to Home Biology Experiments*. Record the answers in the lab section of your science notebook.

Online Lab - Introduction to the Microscopy Lab
Purpose
The purpose of this online lab is to learn about the strengths and capabilities of the four different microscopes available on the microscopy lab bench.

Pre-Reading
↝ Print and read the section of the workbook for the "Introduction to the Microscopy Lab"

online lab.

Procedure

✓ Do the lab entitled "Introduction to the Microscopy Lab" and answer the questions as you work through the online lab.

Lab Notebook

☞ Add the completed workbook pages that were printed to the lab notebook.

Events in Science

Current Events

🕐 Find a current events article relating to the field of biochemistry and complete the article summary sheet found on pg. 246 of the Appendix. Once you are done, add the sheet to the events section of your science notebook.

Historical Figures

🕐 Continue to research the life and work of Aristotle.

Hands-on Activity

Optional Hands-on

✂ Learn about how complimentary base pairs work by creating a DNA ladder out of LEGOS. Directions can be found here: http://elementalblogging.com/homeschool-science-corner-dna/.

Week 2 Supply List

Weekly Experiment	
Supplies from BK01A Biology Kit	☐ Goggles, Coverslips, Forceps, Glycerol, Pipettes, Scalpel, Slide (well), Slides (flat), Stain, methylene blue, Stirring rod (optional)
Additional Supplies From Home	☐ Gloves, Butane lighter (or other flame source), Carrot (raw), Microscope, Microtome (purchased or homemade), Petroleum jelly, Human hair, Pond water, Toothpicks, Vegetable oil (olive or similar), Water, distilled
Hands-on Activity	
Supplies Needed	☐ LEGO bricks

Week 2	Unit 1 (Honors Course)	5-Day

Weekly Topic

→ This week will begin a look at the chemistry of life.

	Day 1	Day 2	Day 3	Day 4	Day 5
Textbook and Experiment	☐ Read *CK-12 Biology* Section 2.1.	☐ Read *CK-12 Biology* Section 2.2.	☐ Read the background and procedure sections for the week's lab.	☐ Do the "Mounting Specimens" lab on pg. 63 in *Illustrated Guide to Home Biology Experiments*.	☐ Do the optional Hands-on Assignment - DNA Ladder.
Writing	☐ Add the vocabulary to the glossary section of your science notebook.	☐ Answer the assigned questions in the reading section of your science notebook.	☐ Take the Chapter 1 Test from *CK-12 Biology*.	☐ Record what you have done in the lab section of your science notebook.	☐ Complete the lab review questions for the week.
Events in Science	☐ Choose one of the Events in Science assignments to do and add your work to the events section of your science notebook.				

Other Notes

Week 2	Unit 1 (Standard Course)	4-Day

Weekly Topic

→ This week will begin a look at the chemistry of life.

	Day 1	Day 2	Day 3	Day 4
Textbook and Experiment	❑ Read *CK-12 Biology* Section 2.1.	❑ Read *CK-12 Biology* Section 2.2.	❑ Read the background and procedure sections for the week's lab.	❑ Do the "Mounting Specimens" lab on pg. 63 in *Illustrated Guide to Home Biology Experiments*. **OR** ❑ Do the online lab "Introduction to the Microscopy Lab."
Writing	❑ Add the vocabulary to the glossary section of your science notebook.	❑ Answer the assigned questions in the reading section of your science notebook.	❑ Take the Chapter 1 Test from *CK-12 Biology*.	❑ Record what you have done in the lab section of your science notebook.

Other Notes

Week 2	Unit 1 (Survey Course)	2-Day

Weekly Topic

→ This week will begin a look at the chemistry of life.

	Day 1	Day 2
Textbook	❒ Read *CK-12 Biology* Section 2.1.	❒ Read *CK-12 Biology* Section 2.2.
Writing	❒ Add the vocabulary to the glossary section of your science notebook. ❒ Take the Chapter 1 Test from *CK-12 Biology*.	❒ Answer the assigned questions in the reading section of your science notebook.
Events in Science	❒ Choose one of the Events in Science assignments to do and add your work to the events section of your science notebook.	

Other Notes

Week 3 Notes - Chemistry of Life, part 2

Textbook Assignments

Reading

📖 *CK-12 Biology* Section 2.3

Written

After you finish reading, answer questions #1-6 in section 2.3 and file your work in the reading section of your science notebook. Then, define the following terms in the glossary section of your science notebook:

- Acid
- Base
- pH
- Polarity

Experiment - Staining

Purpose

The purpose of this lab is to practice and learn various techniques for staining microscope slides.

Pre-Reading

✍ Read the background and procedure sections for the "Staining" lab on pg. 71 in *Illustrated Guide to Home Biology Experiments*.

Procedure

✓ Do the lab entitled "Staining" on pg. 71 in *Illustrated Guide to Home Biology Experiments*.

Lab Notebook

☞ Write down on a sheet of paper or type out your notes as you do the experiment. After you are done, print out your lab notes and add them to the lab section of your science notebook.

Lab Review Questions

🗲 Complete the review questions of the "Staining" lab on pg. 76 in *Illustrated Guide to Home Biology Experiments*. Record the answers in the lab section of your science notebook.

Online Lab - Staining Bacteria

Purpose

The purpose of this online lab is to learn how microbiologists use stain microscope slides to tell different types of bacteria apart.

Pre-Reading

✍ Print and read the section of the workbook for the "Staining Bacteria" online lab.

Procedure

✓ Do the lab entitled "Staining Bacteria" and answer the questions as you work through the online lab.

Lab Notebook

☞ Add the completed workbook pages that were printed to the lab notebook.

Events in Science

Current Events

🕐 Find a current events article relating to the field of biochemistry and complete the article summary sheet found on pg. 246 of the Appendix. Once you are done, add the sheet to the events section of your science notebook.

Historical Figures

🕐 Continue to research the life and work of Aristotle.

Hands-on Activity

Optional Hands-on

✂ Test common household materials to see if they are acids or bases. Directions can be found here: https://elementalscience.com/blogs/science-activities/kitchen-acid-test.

Week 3 Supply List

Weekly Experiment	
Supplies from BK01A Biology Kit	☐ Goggles, Coverslips, Pipettes, Slides (flat), Stain - eosin Y, Stain - Gram's iodine, Stain - Hucker's crystal violet, Stain - methylene blue, Stain - safranin O, Stirring rod (optional)
Additional Supplies From Home	☐ Gloves, Butane lighter (or other flame source), Ethanol 70%, Microscope, Paper towels, Toothpicks, Water, distilled
Hands-on Activity	
Supplies Needed	☐ Red cabbage juice or pH paper, Common household chemicals such as bleach, ammonia, and vinegar

Week 3	Unit 1 (Honors Course)			5-Day

Weekly Topic

→ This week will wrap up a look at the chemistry of life.

	Day 1	Day 2	Day 3	Day 4	Day 5
Textbook and Experiment	❏ Read *CK-12 Biology* Section 2.3.		❏ Read the background and procedure sections for the week's lab.	❏ Do the "Staining" lab on pg. 71 in *Illustrated Guide to Home Biology Experiments*.	❏ Do the optional Hands-on Assignment - Kitchen Acids and Bases.
Writing	❏ Add the vocabulary to the glossary section of your science notebook.	❏ Answer the assigned questions in the reading section of your science notebook.	❏ Take the Chapter 2 Test from *CK-12 Biology*.	❏ Record what you have done in the lab section of your science notebook.	❏ Complete the lab review questions for the week.
Events in Science	❏ Choose one of the Events in Science assignments to do and add your work to the events section of your science notebook.				

Other Notes

Week 3	Unit 1 (Standard Course)		4-Day

Weekly Topic

→ This week will wrap up a look at the chemistry of life.

	Day 1	Day 2	Day 3	Day 4
Textbook and Experiment	❏ Read *CK-12 Biology* Section 2.3.		❏ Read the background and procedure sections for the week's lab.	❏ Do the "Staining" lab on pg. 71 in *Illustrated Guide to Home Biology Experiments*. **OR** ❏ Do the online lab "Staining Bacteria."
Writing	❏ Add the vocabulary to the glossary section of your science notebook.	❏ Answer the assigned questions in the reading section of your science notebook.	❏ Take the Chapter 2 Test from *CK-12 Biology*.	❏ Record what you have done in the lab section of your science notebook.

Other Notes

Week 3	Unit 1 (Survey Course)	2-Day

Weekly Topic

→ This week will wrap up a look at the chemistry of life.

	Day 1	Day 2
Textbook	❑ Read *CK-12 Biology* Section 2.3.	❑ Take the Chapter 2 Test from *CK-12 Biology*.
Writing	❑ Add the vocabulary to the glossary section of your science notebook.	❑ Answer the assigned questions in the reading section of your science notebook.
Events in Science	❑ Choose one of the Events in Science assignments to do and add your work to the events section of your science notebook.	

Other Notes

Week 4 Notes - Cell Structure and Function, part 1

Textbook Assignments
Reading
📖 *CK-12 Biology* Sections 3.1, 3.2

Written
After you finish reading, answer questions #1-3 in section 3.1 and questions #1-4 in section 3.2. File your work in the reading section of your science notebook. Then, define the following terms in the glossary section of your science notebook:

- ☐ Cytoplasm
- ☐ Organelle
- ☐ Plasma membrane
- ☐ Prokaryotic cell
- ☐ Ribosome
- ☐ Virus
- ☐ Endoplasmic reticulum
- ☐ Golgi apparatus
- ☐ Mitochondria
- ☐ Phospholipid bilayer

Experiment - Acids, Bases, and Buffers
Purpose
The purpose of this lab is to learn about the properties of Acids, Bases, and Buffers in cellular systems.

Pre-Reading
✍ Read the background and procedure sections for the "Acids, Bases, and Buffers" lab on pg. 99 in *Illustrated Guide to Home Biology Experiments*.

Procedure
✓ Do the lab entitled "Acids, Bases, and Buffers" on pg. 99 in *Illustrated Guide to Home Biology Experiments*.

Lab Notebook
☞ Write down on a sheet of paper or type out your notes as you do the experiment. After you are done, print out your lab notes and add them to the lab section of your science notebook.

Lab Review Questions
🔥 Complete the review questions of the "Acids, Bases, and Buffers" lab on pg. 107 in *Illustrated Guide to Home Biology Experiments*. Record the answers in the lab section of your science notebook.

Online Lab - Unicellular Eukaryotic Life
Purpose
The purpose of this online lab is to learn about the broad diversity of single-celled eukaryotic life.

Pre-Reading
    ⇝ Print and read the section of the workbook for the "Unicellular Eukaryotic Life" online lab.

Procedure
    ✓ Do the lab entitled "Unicellular Eukaryotic Life" and answer the questions as you work through the online lab.

Lab Notebook
    ☞ Add the completed workbook pages that were printed to the lab notebook.

Events in Science

Current Events
    ⊕ Find a current events article relating to the field of biochemistry and complete the article summary sheet found on pg. 246 of the Appendix. Once you are done, add the sheet to the events section of your science notebook.

Historical Figures
    ⊕ Begin to work on your paper on the life and work of Aristotle. This week, aim to complete your outline and rough draft. See pp. 14-15 for more directions. You will have three weeks to complete this paper.

Hands-on Activity

Optional Hands-on
    ✂ Make a Jell-O model of a cell. Use a margarine container for the cell membrane, Jell-O for cytoplasm, a grape for the nucleus and use your imagination for materials for the remaining organelles.

Week 4 Supply List

Weekly Experiment	
Supplies from BK01A Biology Kit	☐ Goggles, Acetic acid solution, Ammonia solution, Beaker, 50 mL, Centrifuge tubes, 15 mL (5), Hydrochloric acid solution, pH test paper, Pipettes, Reaction plate, 24-well, Reaction plate, 96-well, Sodium hydroxide solution, Stirring rod
Additional Supplies From Home	☐ Gloves, Marking pen, Paper towels, Scissors, Water - distilled
Hands-on Activity	
Supplies Needed	☐ Jell-O, Margarine container, Grape, Other materials for organelles

Week 4	Unit 1 (Honors Course)	5-Day

Weekly Topic

→ This week will begin a look at cell structure and function.

	Day 1	Day 2	Day 3	Day 4	Day 5
Textbook and Experiment	☐ Read *CK-12 Biology* Section 3.1.	☐ Read *CK-12 Biology* Section 3.2.	☐ Read the background and procedure sections for the week's lab.	☐ Do the "Acids, Bases, and Buffers" lab on pg. 99 in *Illustrated Guide to Home Biology Experiments*.	☐ Do the optional Hands-on Assignment - Jell-O Cell.
Writing	☐ Add the vocabulary to the glossary section of your science notebook.	☐ Answer the assigned questions in the reading section of your science notebook.		☐ Record what you have done in the lab section of your science notebook.	☐ Complete the lab review questions for the week.
Events in Science	☐ Choose one of the Events in Science assignments to do and add your work to the events section of your science notebook.				

Other Notes

Week 4	Unit 1 (Standard Course)		4-Day

Weekly Topic

→ This week will begin a look at cell structure and function.

	Day 1	Day 2	Day 3	Day 4
Textbook and Experiment	❏ Read *CK-12 Biology* Section 3.1.	❏ Read *CK-12 Biology* Section 3.2.	❏ Read the background and procedure sections for the week's lab.	❏ Do the "Acids, Bases, and Buffers" lab on pg. 99 in *Illustrated Guide to Home Biology Experiments*. **OR** ❏ Do the online lab "Unicellular Eukaryotic Life."
Writing	❏ Add the vocabulary to the glossary section of your science notebook.	❏ Answer the assigned questions in the reading section of your science notebook.		❏ Record what you have done in the lab section of your science notebook.

Other Notes

Week 4	Unit 1 (Survey Course)	2-Day

Weekly Topic

→ This week will begin a look at cell structure and function.

	Day 1	Day 2
Textbook	❐ Read *CK-12 Biology* Section 3.1.	❐ Read *CK-12 Biology* Section 3.2.
Writing	❐ Add the vocabulary to the glossary section of your science notebook.	❐ Answer the assigned questions in the reading section of your science notebook.
Events in Science	❐ Choose one of the Events in Science assignments to do and add your work to the events section of your science notebook.	

Other Notes

Week 5 Notes - Cell Structure and Function, part 2

Textbook Assignments

Reading
📖 *CK-12 Biology* Section 3.3

Written
After you finish reading, answer questions #1-4 in section 3.3 and file your work in the reading section of your science notebook. Then, define the following terms in the glossary section of your science notebook:

- ☐ Active transport
- ☐ Diffusion
- ☐ Endocytosis
- ☐ Exocytosis
- ☐ Osmosis

Experiment - Carbohydrates and Lipids

Purpose
The purpose of this lab is to explain the roles of Carbohydrates and Lipids and their properties.

Pre-Reading
✍ Read the background and procedure sections for the "Carbohydrates and Lipids" lab on pg. 109 in *Illustrated Guide to Home Biology Experiments*.

Procedure
✓ Do the lab entitled "Carbohydrates and Lipids" on pg. 109 in *Illustrated Guide to Home Biology Experiments*.

Lab Notebook
☞ Write down on a sheet of paper or type out your notes as you do the experiment. After you are done, print out your lab notes and add them to the lab section of your science notebook.

Lab Review Questions
🔖 Complete the review questions of the "Carbohydrates and Lipids" lab on pg. 116 in *Illustrated Guide to Home Biology Experiments*. Record the answers in the lab section of your science notebook.

Online Lab - Introduction to the Molecular Lab

Purpose
The purpose of this online lab is to learn how to perform DNA analysis at the virtual molecular lab bench.

Pre-Reading
✍ Print and read the section of the workbook for the "Introduction to the Molecular Lab" online lab.

Procedure

✓ Do the lab entitled "Introduction to the Molecular Lab" and answer the questions as you work through the online lab.

Lab Notebook

☞ Add the completed workbook pages that were printed to the lab notebook.

Events in Science

Current Events

🕐 Find a current events article relating to the field of biochemistry and complete the article summary sheet found on pg. 246 of the Appendix. Once you are done, add the sheet to the events section of your science notebook.

Historical Figures

🕐 Continue to work on your paper on the life and work of Aristotle. This week, aim to complete your final draft. See pp. 14-15 for more directions.

Hands-on Activity

Optional Hands-on

✂ See osmosis in action using a gummy bear. Place one gummy bear into a glass of water and let it sit overnight. The next morning, take it out and compare its size to that of a gummy bear right out of the package.

Week 5 Supply List

Weekly Experiment	
Supplies from BK01A Biology Kit	☐ Goggles, Barfoed's reagent, Beaker, 250 mL, Benedict's reagent, d-glucose (dextrose), graduated cylinder, 10 mL, Gram's iodine stain, Hydrochloric acid, Pipettes, Reaction plate, 24-well, Seliwanoff's reagent, Slides (flat) and coverslips, Sudan III stain, Test tubes, Test tube rack
Additional Supplies From Home	☐ Gloves, Butane lighter (or other flame source), Butter, Diet sweetener, Fruit juice (unsweetened), Hair dryer (optional), Honey, Isopropanol, Marking pen, Microscope, Microwave oven, Milk (whole), Non-dairy creamer, Onion, Paper bag (brown), Peanut (or cashew, etc.), Potato, Soft drink (Sprite or similar colorless), Sucrose (table sugar), Vegetable oil, Water, distilled
Hands-on Activity	
Supplies Needed	☐ Gummy bears, Glass, Water

Week 5	Unit 1 (Honors Course)			5-Day
	Weekly Topic			
➔ This week will wrap up a look at cell structure and function.				

	Day 1	Day 2	Day 3	Day 4	Day 5
Textbook and Experiment	❒ Read *CK-12 Biology* Section 3.3.		❒ Read the background and procedure sections for the week's lab.	❒ Do the "Carbohydrates and Lipids" lab on pg. 109 in *Illustrated Guide to Home Biology Experiments*.	❒ Do the optional Hands-on Assignment - Gummy Bear Osmosis.
Writing	❒ Add the vocabulary to the glossary section of your science notebook.	❒ Answer the assigned questions in the reading section of your science notebook.	❒ Take the Chapter 3 Test from *CK-12 Biology*.	❒ Record what you have done in the lab section of your science notebook.	❒ Complete the lab review questions for the week.
Events in Science	❒ Choose one of the Events in Science assignments to do and add your work to the events section of your science notebook.				

Other Notes

Week 5	Unit 1 (Standard Course)		4-Day

Weekly Topic

→ This week will wrap up a look at cell structure and function.

	Day 1	Day 2	Day 3	Day 4
Textbook and Experiment	❏ Read *CK-12 Biology* Section 3.3.		❏ Read the background and procedure sections for the week's lab.	❏ Do the "Carbohydrates and Lipids" lab on pg. 109 in *Illustrated Guide to Home Biology Experiments*. **OR** ❏ Do the online lab "Introduction to the Molecular Lab."
Writing	❏ Add the vocabulary to the glossary section of your science notebook.	❏ Answer the assigned questions in the reading section of your science notebook.	❏ Take the Chapter 3 Test from *CK-12 Biology*.	❏ Record what you have done in the lab section of your science notebook.

Other Notes

Week 5	Unit 1 (Survey Course)	2-Day

Weekly Topic

→ This week will wrap up a look at cell structure and function.

	Day 1	Day 2
Textbook	❑ Read *CK-12 Biology* Section 3.3.	❑ Take the Chapter 3 Test from *CK-12 Biology*.
Writing	❑ Add the vocabulary to the glossary section of your science notebook.	❑ Answer the assigned questions in the reading section of your science notebook.
Events in Science	❑ Choose one of the Events in Science assignments to do and add your work to the events section of your science notebook.	

Other Notes

Week 6 Notes - Photosynthesis and Cellular Respiration, part 1

Textbook Assignments

Reading
📖 *CK-12 Biology* Sections 4.1, 4.2

Written
After you finish reading, answer questions #1-5 in section 4.1 and questions #1-6 in section 4.2. File your work in the reading section of your science notebook. Then, define the following terms in the glossary section of your science notebook:

- ☐ Autotroph
- ☐ Cellular respiration
- ☐ Heterotroph
- ☐ Calvin Cycle
- ☐ Chemosynthesis
- ☐ Grana
- ☐ Light reactions
- ☐ Thylakoid membrane

Experiment - Proteins, Enzymes, and Vitamins

Purpose
The purpose of this lab is to investigate Proteins, Enzymes, and Vitamins and discuss their structure and function.

Pre-Reading
✍ Read the background and procedure sections for the "Proteins, Enzymes, and Vitamins" lab on pg. 119 in *Illustrated Guide to Home Biology Experiments*.

Procedure
✓ Do the lab entitled "Proteins, Enzymes, and Vitamins" on pg. 119 in *Illustrated Guide to Home Biology Experiments*.

Lab Notebook
☞ Write down on a sheet of paper or type out your notes as you do the experiment. After you are done, print out your lab notes and add them to the lab section of your science notebook.

Lab Review Questions
🗲 Complete the review questions of the "Proteins, Enzymes, and Vitamins" lab on pg. 128 in *Illustrated Guide to Home Biology Experiments*. Record the answers in the lab section of your science notebook.

Online Lab - Fish Cousins

Purpose
The purpose of this online lab is to use modern molecular biology lab techniques to analyze the relatedness of three fish species.

Pre-Reading
✍ Print and read the section of the workbook for the "Fish Cousins" online lab.

Procedure
- ✓ Do the lab entitled "Fish Cousins" and answer the questions as you work through the online lab.

Lab Notebook
- ☞ Add the completed workbook pages that were printed to the lab notebook.

Events in Science

Current Events
- ⊕ Find a current events article relating to the field of botany and complete the article summary sheet found on pg. 246 of the Appendix. Once you are done, add the sheet to the events section of your science notebook.

Historical Figures
- ⊕ Begin to research the life and work of Antoni van Leeuwenhoek, who is considered by many to be the father of microscopy. You will have three weeks to complete your research. After that, you will have two weeks to prepare a two to three page paper on this scientist and his contributions to the field of biology.

Hands-on Activity

Optional Hands-on
- ✂ See a bit of photosynthesis in action using a leaf and a bowl filled with water. Directions for this project can be found here: https://www.pinterest.com/pin/192036371587791960/.

Week 6 Supply List

Weekly Experiment	
Supplies from BK01A Biology Kit	❏ Goggles, Ascorbic acid tablet, Beaker - 100 mL, Beaker - 250 mL, Biuret reagent, Centrifuge tubes - 15 mL, Gelatin (unflavored), Gram's iodine stain, Graduated cylinder - 10 mL, Graduated cylinder - 100 mL, Hydrochloric acid, Lead(II) acetate, l-Glutamine, pH test paper, Pipettes, Reaction plate 24-well, Reaction plate 96-well, Sodium hydroxide, Spatula, Stirring rod, Test tubes, Test tube clamp, Test tube rack
Additional Supplies From Home	❏ Gloves, Blood from uncooked meat, Desk lamp or other strong light source, Egg white, raw, Freezer, Hydrogen peroxide 3%, Isopropanol 99%, Marking pen, Microwave oven, Paper or cloth, black, Paper towels, Starch water, Urine specimen(s), Water - distilled
Hands-on Activity	
Supplies Needed	❏ Leaf, Bowl, Water

Week 6	Unit 1 (Honors Course)			5-Day

Weekly Topic

→ This week will begin a look at photosynthesis and cellular respiration.

	Day 1	Day 2	Day 3	Day 4	Day 5
Textbook and Experiment	☐ Read *CK-12 Biology* Section 4.1.	☐ Read *CK-12 Biology* Section 4.2.	☐ Read the background and procedure sections for the week's lab.	☐ Do the "Proteins, Enzymes, and Vitamins" lab on pg. 119 in *Illustrated Guide to Home Biology Experiments*.	☐ Do the optional Hands-on Assignment - Photosynthesis in Action.
Writing	☐ Add the vocabulary to the glossary section of your science notebook.	☐ Answer the assigned questions in the reading section of your science notebook.		☐ Record what you have done in the lab section of your science notebook.	☐ Complete the lab review questions for the week.
Events in Science	☐ Choose one of the Events in Science assignments to do and add your work to the events section of your science notebook.				

Other Notes

Week 6	Unit 1 (Standard Course)		4-Day
Weekly Topic			

→ This week will begin a look at photosynthesis and cellular respiration.

	Day 1	Day 2	Day 3	Day 4
Textbook and Experiment	☐ Read *CK-12 Biology* Section 4.1.	☐ Read *CK-12 Biology* Section 4.2.	☐ Read the background and procedure sections for the week's lab.	☐ Do the "Proteins, Enzymes, and Vitamins" lab on pg. 119 in *Illustrated Guide to Home Biology Experiments.* **OR** ☐ Do the online lab "Fish Cousins."
Writing	☐ Add the vocabulary to the glossary section of your science notebook.	☐ Answer the assigned questions in the reading section of your science notebook.		☐ Record what you have done in the lab section of your science notebook.

Other Notes

Week 6	Unit 1 (Survey Course)	2-Day

Weekly Topic

➔ This week will begin a look at photosynthesis and cellular respiration.

	Day 1	Day 2
Textbook	❑ Read *CK-12 Biology* Section 4.1.	❑ Read *CK-12 Biology* Section 4.2.
Writing	❑ Add the vocabulary to the glossary section of your science notebook.	❑ Answer the assigned questions in the reading section of your science notebook.
Events in Science	❑ Choose one of the Events in Science assignments to do and add your work to the events section of your science notebook.	

Other Notes

Week 7 Notes - Photosynthesis and Cellular Respiration, part 2

Textbook Assignments

Reading
📖 *CK-12 Biology* Sections 4.3, 4.4

Written
After you finish reading, answer questions #1-7 in section 4.3 and questions #1-5 in section 4.4. File your work in the reading section of your science notebook. Then, define the following terms in the glossary section of your science notebook:

- Aerobic respiration
- Anaerobic respiration
- Glycolysis
- Krebs cycle
- Alcoholic fermentation
- Lactic fermentation

Experiment - Observing Specialized Eukaryotic Cells

Purpose
The purpose of this lab is to observe Specialized Eukaryotic cells.

Pre-Reading
✍ Read the background and procedure sections for the "Observing Specialized Eukaryotic Cells" lab on pg. 217 in *Illustrated Guide to Home Biology Experiments*.

Procedure
✓ Do the lab entitled "Observing Specialized Eukaryotic Cells" on pg. 217 in *Illustrated Guide to Home Biology Experiments*.

Lab Notebook
☞ Write down on a sheet of paper or type out your notes as you do the experiment. After you are done, print out your lab notes and add them to the lab section of your science notebook.

Lab Review Questions
🕯 Complete the review questions of the "Observing Specialized Eukaryotic Cells" lab on pg. 220 in *Illustrated Guide to Home Biology Experiments*. Record the answers in the lab section of your science notebook.

Online Lab - Shark Fin Sequencing

Purpose
The purpose of this online lab is to determine if great white sharks are being fished illegally in nearby waters.

Pre-Reading
✍ Print and read the section of the workbook for the "Shark Fin Sequencing" online lab.

Procedure
✓ Do the lab entitled "Shark Fin Sequencing" and answer the questions as you work

through the online lab.

Lab Notebook

☞ Add the completed workbook pages that were printed to the lab notebook.

Events in Science

Current Events

🕐 Find a current events article relating to the field of botany and complete the article summary sheet found on pg. 246 of the Appendix. Once you are done, add the sheet to the events section of your science notebook.

Historical Figures

🕐 Continue to research the life and work of Antoni van Leeuwenhoek.

Hands-on Activity

Optional Hands-on

✂ Watch yeast ferment sugar, which is an example of anaerobic respiration. Add a teaspoon of sugar to a cup of water and stir until the sugar dissolves. Then, sprinkle a teaspoon of yeast on the top and watch what happens.

Week 7 Supply List

Weekly Experiment	
Supplies from BK01A Biology Kit	☐ Goggles, Forceps, Slides (flat) and coverslips, Eosin Y, Gram's iodine, Hucker's crystal violet, Methylene blue, Safranin O, Sudan III
Additional Supplies From Home	☐ Gloves, Elodea leaf, Microscope, Onion - raw, Prepared slides (see Note), Water, distilled
Hands-on Activity	
Supplies Needed	☐ Bowl, Water, Sugar, Yeast

Week 7	Unit 1 (Honors Course)			5-Day

Weekly Topic

→ This week will wrap up a look at photosynthesis and cellular respiration.

	Day 1	Day 2	Day 3	Day 4	Day 5
Textbook and Experiment	☐ Read *CK-12 Biology* Section 4.3.	☐ Read *CK-12 Biology* Section 4.4.	☐ Read the background and procedure sections for the week's lab.	☐ Do the "Observing Specialized Eukaryotic Cells" lab on pg. 217 in *Illustrated Guide to Home Biology Experiments*.	☐ Do the optional Hands-on Assignment - Anaerobic Respiration.
Writing	☐ Add the vocabulary to the glossary section of your science notebook.	☐ Answer the assigned questions in the reading section of your science notebook.		☐ Record what you have done in the lab section of your science notebook.	☐ Complete the lab review questions for the week.
Events in Science	☐ Choose one of the Events in Science assignments to do and add your work to the events section of your science notebook.				

Other Notes

Week 7	Unit 1 (Standard Course)		4-Day

Weekly Topic

→ This week will wrap up a look at photosynthesis and cellular respiration.

	Day 1	Day 2	Day 3	Day 4
Textbook and Experiment	❑ Read *CK-12 Biology* Section 4.3.	❑ Read *CK-12 Biology* Section 4.4.	❑ Read the background and procedure sections for the week's lab.	❑ Do the "Observing Specialized Eukaryotic Cells" lab on pg. 217 in *Illustrated Guide to Home Biology Experiments.* **OR** ❑ Do the online lab "Shark Fin Sequencing."
Writing	❑ Add the vocabulary to the glossary section of your science notebook.	❑ Answer the assigned questions in the reading section of your science notebook.		❑ Record what you have done in the lab section of your science notebook.

Other Notes

Week 7	Unit 1 (Survey Course)	2-Day

Weekly Topic

→ This week will wrap up a look at photosynthesis and cellular respiration.

	Day 1	Day 2
Textbook	☐ Read *CK-12 Biology* Section 4.3.	☐ Read *CK-12 Biology* Section 4.4.
Writing	☐ Add the vocabulary to the glossary section of your science notebook.	☐ Answer the assigned questions in the reading section of your science notebook.
Events in Science	☐ Choose one of the Events in Science assignments to do and add your work to the events section of your science notebook.	

Other Notes

Week 8 Notes - Cell Cycles

Textbook Assignments

Reading

📖 *CK-12 Biology* Section 5.1

Written

After you finish reading, answer questions #1-6 in section 5.1 and file your work in the reading section of your science notebook. Then, define the following terms in the glossary section of your science notebook:

- ☐ Binary fission
- ☐ Cancer
- ☐ Cytokinesis
- ☐ Interphase
- ☐ Mitosis
- ☐ Tumor

Experiment - Chlorophyll and Photosynthesis

Purpose

The purpose of this lab is to explain the process of photosynthesis and the role of chlorophyll.

Pre-Reading

✍ Read the background and procedure sections for the "Chlorophyll and Photosynthesis" lab on pg. 157 in *Illustrated Guide to Home Biology Experiments*.

Procedure

✓ Do the lab entitled "Chlorophyll & Photosynthesis" on pg. 157 in *Illustrated Guide to Home Biology Experiments*.

Lab Notebook

☞ Write down on a sheet of paper or type out your notes as you do the experiment. After you are done, print out your lab notes and add them to the lab section of your science notebook.

Lab Review Questions

🖊 Complete the review questions of the "Chlorophyll & Photosynthesis" lab on pg. 163 in *Illustrated Guide to Home Biology Experiments*. Record the answers in the lab section of your science notebook.

Online Lab - Parasites

Purpose

The purpose of this online lab is to compare how parasites obtain nutrition from their hosts, and learn how different parasites species are related.

Pre-Reading

✍ Print and read the section of the workbook for the "Parasites" online lab.

Procedure
- ✓ Do the lab entitled "Parasites" and answer the questions as you work through the online lab.

Lab Notebook
- ☞ Add the completed workbook pages that were printed to the lab notebook.

Events in Science

Current Events
- ⏱ Find a current events article relating to the field of molecular biology and complete the article summary sheet found on pg. 246 of the Appendix. Once you are done, add the sheet to the events section of your science notebook.

Historical Figures
- ⏱ Continue to research the life and work of Antoni van Leeuwenhoek.

Hands-on Activity

Optional Hands-on
- ✂ Dissect a haploid cell, a.k.a. an egg. Use the following website to identify the different parts of a chicken egg: https://www.scienceofcooking.com/eggs/anatomy-of-a-chicken-egg.html.

Week 8 Supply List

Weekly Experiment	
Supplies from BK01A Biology Kit	☐ Goggles, Beaker - 250 mL, Bromothymol blue, Centrifuge tubes - 15 mL, Centrifuge tubes - 50 mL, Chromatography paper, Forceps, Gram's iodine stain, Hydrochloric acid, Pipettes, Ruler (mm scale), Slides (flat) and coverslips, Test tube clamp, Test tube rack, Thermometer
Additional Supplies From Home	☐ Gloves, Coin with milled edge (optional), Cotton balls, Elodea (water weed; see text), Isopropanol 70%, Leaves, Light source (see text), Meter stick or measuring tape, Microscope, Microwave oven, Saucer, Scissors, Soda straw, Toothpicks (plastic), UV light source (optional), Watch or clock with second hand, Water - distilled
Hands-on Activity	
Supplies Needed	☐ Chicken egg

Week 8		Unit 1 (Honors Course)			5-Day

Weekly Topic

➔ This week will look at cell cycles.

	Day 1	Day 2	Day 3	Day 4	Day 5
Textbook and Experiment	❑ Read *CK-12 Biology* Section 5.1.		❑ Read the background and procedure sections for the week's lab.	❑ Do the "Chlorophyll and Photosynthesis" lab on pg. 157 in *Illustrated Guide to Home Biology Experiments*.	❑ Do the optional Hands-on Assignment - Egg Dissection.
Writing	❑ Add the vocabulary to the glossary section of your science notebook.	❑ Answer the assigned questions in the reading section of your science notebook.	❑ Take the Chapter 4 Test from *CK-12 Biology*.	❑ Record what you have done in the lab section of your science notebook.	❑ Complete the lab review questions for the week.
Events in Science	❑ Choose one of the Events in Science assignments to do and add your work to the events section of your science notebook.				

Other Notes

Week 8	Unit 1 (Standard Course)		4-Day

Weekly Topic

→ This week will look at cell cycles.

	Day 1	Day 2	Day 3	Day 4
Textbook and Experiment	❏ Read *CK-12 Biology* Section 5.1.		❏ Read the background and procedure sections for the week's lab.	❏ Do the "Chlorophyll and Photosynthesis" lab on pg. 157 in *Illustrated Guide to Home Biology Experiments.* **OR** ❏ Do the online lab "Parasites."
Writing	❏ Add the vocabulary to the glossary section of your science notebook.	❏ Answer the assigned questions in the reading section of your science notebook.	❏ Take the Chapter 4 Test from *CK-12 Biology.*	❏ Record what you have done in the lab section of your science notebook.

Other Notes

Week 8	Unit 1 (Survey Course)	2-Day

Weekly Topic

→ This week will look at cell cycles.

	Day 1	Day 2
Textbook	☐ Read *CK-12 Biology* Section 5.1.	☐ Take the Chapter 4 Test from *CK-12 Biology*.
Writing	☐ Add the vocabulary to the glossary section of your science notebook.	☐ Answer the assigned questions in the reading section of your science notebook.
Events in Science	☐ Choose one of the Events in Science assignments to do and add your work to the events section of your science notebook.	

Other Notes

Week 9 Notes - Mitosis

Textbook Assignments

Reading

    📖 *CK-12 Biology* Section 5.2

Written

After you finish reading, answer questions #1-6 in section 5.2 and file your work in the reading section of your science notebook. Then, define the following terms in the glossary section of your science notebook:

- ☐ Anaphase
- ☐ Centromere
- ☐ Chromatid
- ☐ Chromatin
- ☐ Homologous chromosomes
- ☐ Metaphase
- ☐ Prophase
- ☐ Telophase

Experiment - Investigating Osmosis

Purpose

The purpose of this lab is to explain the process of osmosis and observe cells during osmosis.

Pre-Reading

    ✍ Read the background and procedure sections for the "Investigating Osmosis" lab on pg. 167 in *Illustrated Guide to Home Biology Experiments*.

Procedure

    ✓ Do the lab entitled "Investigating Osmosis" on pg. 167 in *Illustrated Guide to Home Biology Experiments*.

Lab Notebook

    ☞ Write down on a sheet of paper or type out your notes as you do the experiment. After you are done, print out your lab notes and add them to the lab section of your science notebook.

Lab Review Questions

    🐾 Complete the review questions of the "Investigating Osmosis" lab on pg. 167 in *Illustrated Guide to Home Biology Experiments*. Record the answers in the lab section of your science notebook.

Online Lab - TEM & Membranes

Purpose

The purpose of this online lab is to learn how transmission electron microscopy works, and how similar structures can appear at different levels of organization.

Pre-Reading

    ✍ Print and read the section of the workbook for the "TEM & Membranes" online lab.

Procedure
✓ Do the lab entitled "TEM & Membranes" and answer the questions as you work through the online lab.

Lab Notebook
☞ Add the completed workbook pages that were printed to the lab notebook.

Events in Science

Current Events
🕐 Find a current events article relating to the field of molecular biology and complete the article summary sheet found on pg. 246 of the Appendix. Once you are done, add the sheet to the events section of your science notebook.

Historical Figures
🕐 Begin to work on your paper on the life and work of Antoni van Leeuwenhoek. This week, aim to complete your outline and rough draft. See pp. 14-15 for more directions. You will have three weeks to complete this paper.

Hands-on Activity

Optional Hands-on
✂ Make a poster depicting the different phases of mitosis using pipe cleaners for your chromosomes.

Week 9 Supply List

Weekly Experiment	
Supplies from BK01A Biology Kit	❒ None
Additional Supplies From Home	❒ Gloves, Balance, Eggs, uncooked (2), Foam cups, Graph paper, calculator, or software, Marking pen, Paper towels, Syrup (corn, maple, pancake, waffle, etc.), Tablespoons, plastic or metal (2), Vinegar - distilled white, Watch or clock with second hand
Hands-on Activity	
Supplies Needed	❒ Pipe cleaners, Poster board

Week 9	Unit 1 (Honors Course)			5-Day
Weekly Topic				

➜ This week will look at mitosis.

	Day 1	Day 2	Day 3	Day 4	Day 5
Textbook and Experiment	❐ Read *CK-12 Biology* Section 5.2.		❐ Read the background and procedure sections for the week's lab.	❐ Do the "Investigating Osmosis" lab on pg. 167 in *Illustrated Guide to Home Biology Experiments.*	❐ Do the optional Hands-on Assignment - Mitosis Poster.
Writing	❐ Add the vocabulary to the glossary section of your science notebook.	❐ Answer the assigned questions in the reading section of your science notebook.		❐ Record what you have done in the lab section of your science notebook.	❐ Complete the lab review questions for the week.
Events in Science	❐ Choose one of the Events in Science assignments to do and add your work to the events section of your science notebook.				

Other Notes

Week 9	Unit 1 (Standard Course)		4-Day

Weekly Topic

→ This week will look at mitosis.

	Day 1	Day 2	Day 3	Day 4
Textbook and Experiment	❐ Read *CK-12 Biology* Section 5.2.		❐ Read the background and procedure sections for the week's lab.	❐ Do the "Investigating Osmosis" lab on pg. 167 in *Illustrated Guide to Home Biology Experiments*. **OR** ❐ Do the online lab "TEM & Membranes."
Writing	❐ Add the vocabulary to the glossary section of your science notebook.	❐ Answer the assigned questions in the reading section of your science notebook.		❐ Record what you have done in the lab section of your science notebook.

Other Notes

Week 9	Unit 1 (Survey Course)	2-Day

Weekly Topic

➜ This week will look at mitosis.

	Day 1	Day 2
Textbook	❑ Read *CK-12 Biology* Section 5.2.	
Writing	❑ Add the vocabulary to the glossary section of your science notebook.	❑ Answer the assigned questions in the reading section of your science notebook.
Events in Science	❑ Choose one of the Events in Science assignments to do and add your work to the events section of your science notebook.	

Other Notes

Week 10 Notes - Meiosis

Textbook Assignments

Reading
📖 *CK-12 Biology* Section 5.3

Written
After you finish reading, answer questions #1-7 in section 5.3 and file your work in the reading section of your science notebook. Then, define the following terms in the glossary section of your science notebook:

- ☐ Crossing-over
- ☐ Diploid
- ☐ Fertilization
- ☐ Gamete
- ☐ Gametogenesis
- ☐ Haploid
- ☐ Independent Assortment
- ☐ Meiosis
- ☐ Sexual reproduction
- ☐ Zygote

Experiment - Investigating Cell Division
The purpose of this lab is to explain the process of cell division and observe cells during division.

Pre-Reading
✍ Read the background and procedure sections for the "Investigating Cell Division" lab on pg. 173 in *Illustrated Guide to Home Biology Experiments*.

Procedure
✓ Do the lab entitled "Investigating Cell Division" on pg. 173 in *Illustrated Guide to Home Biology Experiments*.

Lab Notebook
☞ Write down on a sheet of paper or type out your notes as you do the experiment. After you are done, print out your lab notes and add them to the lab section of your science notebook.

Lab Review Questions
🦷 Complete the review questions of the "Investigating Cell Division" lab on pg. 181 in *Illustrated Guide to Home Biology Experiments*. Record the answers in the lab section of your science notebook.

Online Lab
☞ There is no online lab scheduled for this week.

Events in Science

Current Events
🕐 Find a current events article relating to the field of molecular biology and complete the

article summary sheet found on pg. 246 of the Appendix. Once you are done, add the sheet to the events section of your science notebook.

Historical Figures

⊕ Continue to work on your paper on the life and work of Antoni van Leeuwenhoek. This week, aim to complete your final draft. See pp. 14-15 for more directions.

Hands-on Activity

Optional Hands-on

✂ Make a poster depicting the different phases of meiosis using pipe cleaners for your chromosomes.

Week 10 Supply List

Weekly Experiment	
Supplies from BK01A Biology Kit	☐ None
Additional Supplies From Home	☐ Microscope (oil-immersion if available), Prepared slide: plant mitosis (onion tip), Prepared slide: animal mitosis (optional)
Hands-on Activity	
Supplies Needed	☐ Pipe cleaners, Poster board

Week 10	Unit 1 (Honors Course)	5-Day

Weekly Topic

➜ This week will be an introduction to biology.

	Day 1	Day 2	Day 3	Day 4	Day 5
Textbook and Experiment	❑ Read *CK-12 Biology* Section 5.3.		❑ Read the background and procedure sections for the week's lab.	❑ Do the "Investigating Cell Division" lab on pg. 173 in *Illustrated Guide to Home Biology Experiments*.	❑ Do the optional Hands-on Assignment - Meiosis Poster.
Writing	❑ Add the vocabulary to the glossary section of your science notebook.	❑ Answer the assigned questions in the reading section of your science notebook.	❑ Take the Chapter 5 Test from *CK-12 Biology*.	❑ Record what you have done in the lab section of your science notebook.	❑ Complete the lab review questions for the week.
Events in Science	❑ Choose one of the Events in Science assignments to do and add your work to the events section of your science notebook.				

Other Notes

Week 10	Unit 1 (Standard Course)		4-Day

Weekly Topic

→ This week will be an introduction to biology.

	Day 1	Day 2	Day 3	Day 4
Textbook and Experiment	❏ Read *CK-12 Biology* Section 5.3.		❏ Read the background and procedure sections for the week's lab.	❏ Do the "Investigating Cell Division" lab on pg. 173 in *Illustrated Guide to Home Biology Experiments*.
Writing	❏ Add the vocabulary to the glossary section of your science notebook.	❏ Answer the assigned questions in the reading section of your science notebook.	❏ Take the Chapter 5 Test from *CK-12 Biology*.	❏ Record what you have done in the lab section of your science notebook.

Other Notes

Week 10	Unit 1 (Survey Course)	2-Day

Weekly Topic

→ This week will be an introduction to biology.

	Day 1	Day 2
Textbook	❏ Read *CK-12 Biology* Section 5.3.	❏ Take the Chapter 5 Test from *CK-12 Biology*.
Writing	❏ Add the vocabulary to the glossary section of your science notebook.	❏ Answer the assigned questions in the reading section of your science notebook.
Events in Science	❏ Choose one of the Events in Science assignments to do and add your work to the events section of your science notebook.	

Other Notes

Biology for High School

Unit 2 - Genetics and Evolution

Week 1 Notes - Gregor Mendel and Genetics

Textbook Assignments
Reading
📖 *CK-12 Biology* Sections 6.1, 6.2
Written
After you finish reading, answer questions #1-7 in section 6.1 and questions #1-4 in section 6.2. File your work in the reading section of your science notebook. Then, define the following terms in the glossary section of your science notebook:

- Allele
- Dominant allele
- Genotype
- Heterozygote
- Homozygote
- Law of Independent Assortment
- Phenotype
- Recessive allele
- Co-dominance
- Punnett square

Experiment - Exploring Mendelian Genetics
Purpose
The purpose of this lab is to explain and explore Mendelian Genetics.
Pre-Reading
✍ Read the background and procedure sections for the "Exploring Mendelian Genetics" lab on pg. 213 in *Illustrated Guide to Home Biology Experiments*.
Procedure
✓ Do the lab entitled "Exploring Mendelian Genetics" on pg. 213 in *Illustrated Guide to Home Biology Experiments*.
Lab Notebook
☞ Write down on a sheet of paper or type out your notes as you do the experiment. After you are done, print out your lab notes and add them to the lab section of your science notebook.
Lab Questions
🔖 Complete the review questions of the "Exploring Mendelian Genetics" lab on pg. 215 in *Illustrated Guide to Home Biology Experiments*. Record the answers in the lab section of your science notebook.

Online Lab - Introduction to the Genetics Lab
Purpose
The purpose of this online lab is to introduce yourself to the virtual Genetics lab to discover how pea plants display Mendelian inheritance patterns.
Pre-Reading
✍ Print and read the section of the workbook for the "Introduction to the Genetics Lab"

online lab.

Procedure

✓ Do the lab entitled "Introduction to the Genetics Lab" and answer the questions as you work through the online lab.

Lab Notebook

☞ Add the completed workbook pages that were printed to the lab notebook.

Events in Science

Current Events

🕐 Find a current events article relating to the field of genetics and complete the article summary sheet found on pg. 246 of the Appendix. Once you are done, add the sheet to the events section of your science notebook.

Historical Figures

🕐 Begin to research the life and work of Gregor Mendel, who is considered by many to be the father of genetics. You will have three weeks to complete your research. After that, you will have two weeks to prepare a two to three page paper on this scientist and his contributions to the field of biology.

Hands-on Activity

Optional Hands-on

✂ Practice creating a Punnett square with LEGOS and a worksheet. Directions for this can be found here: http://elementalblogging.com/punnett-square/.

Week 1 Supply List

Weekly Experiment	
Supplies from BK01A Biology Kit	❑ Phenylthiocarbamide (PTC) test strips
Additional Supplies From Home	❑ None
Hands-on Activity	
Supplies Needed	❑ LEGOS

Week 1	Unit 2 (Honors Course)			5-Day

Weekly Topic

➔ This week will look at Gregor Mendel and genetics.

	Day 1	Day 2	Day 3	Day 4	Day 5
Textbook and Experiment	❑ Read *CK-12 Biology* Section 6.1.	❑ Read *CK-12 Biology* Section 6.2.	❑ Read the background and procedure sections for the week's lab.	❑ Do the "Exploring Mendelian Genetics" lab on pg. 213 in *Illustrated Guide to Home Biology Experiments*.	❑ Do the optional Hands-on Assignment - Punnett Square.
Writing	❑ Add the vocabulary to the glossary section of your science notebook.	❑ Answer the assigned questions in the reading section of your science notebook.		❑ Record what you have done in the lab section of your science notebook.	❑ Complete the lab review questions for the week.
Events in Science	❑ Choose one of the Events in Science assignments to do and add your work to the events section of your science notebook.				

Other Notes

Week 1	Unit 2 (Standard Course)	4-Day

Weekly Topic

→ This week will look at Gregor Mendel and genetics.

	Day 1	Day 2	Day 3	Day 4
Textbook and Experiment	❑ Read *CK-12 Biology* Section 6.1.	❑ Read *CK-12 Biology* Section 6.2.	❑ Read the background and procedure sections for the week's lab.	❑ Do the "Exploring Mendelian Genetics" lab on pg. 213 in *Illustrated Guide to Home Biology Experiments.* **OR** ❑ Do the online lab "Introduction to the Genetics Lab."
Writing	❑ Add the vocabulary to the glossary section of your science notebook.	❑ Answer the assigned questions in the reading section of your science notebook.		❑ Record what you have done in the lab section of your science notebook.

Other Notes

Week 1	Unit 2 (Survey Course)	2-Day

Weekly Topic

→ This week will look at Gregor Mendel and genetics.

	Day 1	Day 2
Textbook	❑ Read *CK-12 Biology* Section 6.1.	❑ Read *CK-12 Biology* Section 6.2.
Writing	❑ Add the vocabulary to the glossary section of your science notebook.	❑ Answer the assigned questions in the reading section of your science notebook.
Events in Science	❑ Choose one of the Events in Science assignments to do and add your work to the events section of your science notebook.	

Other Notes

Week 2 Notes - Molecular Genetics, part 1

Textbook Assignments

Reading
📖 *CK-12 Biology* Sections 7.1, 7.2

Written
After you finish reading, answer questions #1-6 in section 7.1 and questions #1-4 in section 7.2. File your work in the reading section of your science notebook. Then, define the following terms in the glossary section of your science notebook:

- ☐ Chargaff's Rules
- ☐ mRNA
- ☐ rRNA
- ☐ tRNA
- ☐ Codon
- ☐ Transcription
- ☐ Translation

Experiment - Extracting, Isolating, and Visualizing DNA

Purpose
The purpose of this lab is to look at DNA and determine its properties and traits.

Pre-Reading
✍ Read the background and procedure sections for the "Extracting, Isolating and Visualizing DNA" lab on pg. 137 in *Illustrated Guide to Home Biology Experiments*.

Procedure
✓ Do the lab entitled "Extracting, Isolating and Visualizing DNA" on pg. 137 in *Illustrated Guide to Home Biology Experiments*.

Lab Notebook
☞ Write down on a sheet of paper or type out your notes as you do the experiment. After you are done, print out your lab notes and add them to the lab section of your science notebook.

Lab Questions
🖋 Complete the review questions of the "Extracting, Isolating and Visualizing DNA" lab on pg. 137 in *Illustrated Guide to Home Biology Experiments*. Record the answers in the lab section of your science notebook.

Online Lab - Labrador Fur Color Inheritance

Purpose
The purpose of this online lab is to determine the pattern of inheritance of coat color in Labrador retrievers.

Pre-Reading
✍ Print and read the section of the workbook for the "Labrador Fur Color Inheritance" online lab.

Procedure

✓ Do the lab entitled "Labrador Fur Color Inheritance" and answer the questions as you work through the online lab.

Lab Notebook

☞ Add the completed workbook pages that were printed to the lab notebook.

Events in Science

Current Events

🕘 Find a current events article relating to the field of genetics and complete the article summary sheet found on pg. 246 of the Appendix. Once you are done, add the sheet to the events section of your science notebook.

Historical Figures

🕘 Continue to research the life and work of Gregor Mendel.

Hands-on Activity

Optional Hands-on

✂ Use Easter eggs and M&M's to practice genetic recombination. Directions for this project can be found here: http://science-mattersblog.blogspot.com/2011/04/genetics-easter-egg-genetics.html.

Week 2 Supply List

Weekly Experiment	
Supplies from BK01A Biology Kit	❏ Goggles, Centrifuge tubes - 50 mL, Coverslips, Eosin Y stain, Funnel, Graduated cylinder - 10 mL, Methylene blue stain, Microscope slides (flat), Pipettes, Reaction plate 96-well, Scalpel, Sodium dodecyl sulfate 10%, Spatula, Stirring rod, Test tubes, Test tube rack, Yeast (optional)
Additional Supplies From Home	❏ Gloves, Balance (optional), Beef or pork liver, raw (or yeast), Cheesecloth (or muslin, etc.), Isopropanol (see text), Freezer, Microscope, Paper towels, Saucer, Table salt, Teaspoon, Toothpick, Water - distilled
Hands-on Activity	
Supplies Needed	❏ Easter eggs, M&M's

Week 2	Unit 2 (Honors Course)			5-Day

Weekly Topic

→ This week will begin a look at molecular genetics.

	Day 1	Day 2	Day 3	Day 4	Day 5
Textbook and Experiment	❏ Read *CK-12 Biology* Section 7.1.	❏ Read *CK-12 Biology* Section 7.2.	❏ Read the background and procedure sections for the week's lab.	❏ Do the "Extracting, Isolating and Visualizing DNA" lab on pg. 137 in *Illustrated Guide to Home Biology Experiments*.	❏ Do the optional Hands-on Assignment - Easter Egg Genetics.
Writing	❏ Add the vocabulary to the glossary section of your science notebook.	❏ Answer the assigned questions in the reading section of your science notebook.	❏ Take the Chapter 6 Test from *CK-12 Biology*.	❏ Record what you have done in the lab section of your science notebook.	❏ Complete the lab review questions for the week.
Events in Science	❏ Choose one of the Events in Science assignments to do and add your work to the events section of your science notebook.				

Other Notes

Week 2	Unit 2 (Standard Course)	4-Day

Weekly Topic
→ This week will begin a look at molecular genetics.

	Day 1	Day 2	Day 3	Day 4
Textbook and Experiment	❏ Read *CK-12 Biology* Section 7.1.	❏ Read *CK-12 Biology* Section 7.2.	❏ Read the background and procedure sections for the week's lab.	❏ Do the "Extracting, Isolating and Visualizing DNA" lab on pg. 137 in *Illustrated Guide to Home Biology Experiments*. **OR** ❏ Do the online lab "Labrador Fur Color Inheritance."
Writing	❏ Add the vocabulary to the glossary section of your science notebook.	❏ Answer the assigned questions in the reading section of your science notebook.	❏ Take the Chapter 6 Test from *CK-12 Biology*.	❏ Record what you have done in the lab section of your science notebook.

Other Notes

Week 2	Unit 2 (Survey Course)		2-Day

Weekly Topic

→ This week will begin a look at molecular genetics.

	Day 1	Day 2
Textbook	❑ Read *CK-12 Biology* Section 7.1.	❑ Read *CK-12 Biology* Section 7.2.
Writing	❑ Add the vocabulary to the glossary section of your science notebook. ❑ Take the Chapter 6 Test from *CK-12 Biology*.	❑ Answer the assigned questions in the reading section of your science notebook.
Events in Science	❑ Choose one of the Events in Science assignments to do and add your work to the events section of your science notebook.	

Other Notes

Week 3 Notes - Molecular Genetics, part 2

Textbook Assignments
Reading
📖 *CK-12 Biology* Sections 7.3, 7.4

Written
After you finish reading, answer questions #1-6 in section 7.3 and questions #1-4 in section 7.4. File your work in the reading section of your science notebook. Then, define the following terms in the glossary section of your science notebook:

- ☐ Chromosomal alteration
- ☐ Frameshift mutation
- ☐ Germline mutation
- ☐ Mutagen
- ☐ Point mutation
- ☐ Somatic mutation
- ☐ Homeobox gene
- ☐ Operon
- ☐ TATA box

Experiment - Build a Gel Electrophoresis Apparatus
Purpose
The purpose of this lab is to extract DNA and separate the DNA based upon size.

Pre-Reading
↪ Read the background and procedure sections for the "Build a Gel Electrophoresis Apparatus" lab on pg. 143 in *Illustrated Guide to Home Biology Experiments*.

Procedure
✓ Do the lab entitled "Build a Gel Electrophoresis Apparatus" on pg. 143 in *Illustrated Guide to Home Biology Experiments*.

Lab Notebook
☞ Write down on a sheet of paper or type out your notes as you do the experiment. After you are done, print out your lab notes and add them to the lab section of your science notebook.

Lab Questions
🖋 There are no lab review questions for this lab.

Online Lab - Colorblindness Inheritance
Purpose
The purpose of this online lab is to use the virtual Genetics lab room to learn how colorblindness is inherited.

Pre-Reading
↪ Print and read the section of the workbook for the "Colorblindness Inheritance" online lab.

Procedure
✓ Do the lab entitled "Colorblindness Inheritance" and answer the questions as you work through the online lab.

Lab Notebook
☞ Add the completed workbook pages that were printed to the lab notebook.

Events in Science
Current Events
🕐 Find a current events article relating to the field of genetics and complete the article summary sheet found on pg. 246 of the Appendix. Once you are done, add the sheet to the events section of your science notebook.

Historical Figures
🕐 Continue to research the life and work of Gregor Mendel.

Hands-on Activity
Optional Hands-on
✂ Extract DNA from fruit. You will need a piece of banana or strawberry, dish soap, salt, ice-cold isopropyl alcohol (70% or higher), zipper-style plastic bag, coffee filter, funnel, wooden coffee stirrer, and a clear glass for the extraction process. Directions for this lab can be found here: http://sassafrasscience.com/extracting-dna-uncle-cecil/.

Week 3 Supply List

Weekly Experiment	
Supplies from BK01A Biology Kit	☐ Leads, alligator clip (2), Ruler
Additional Supplies From Home	☐ Aluminum foil, Batteries - 9V transistor (5, 7, or 9), Gel casting comb materials, Marking pen (Sharpie or similar), Plastic containers, Scissors, Tape (electrical or masking)
Hands-on Activity	
Supplies Needed	☐ A piece of banana or strawberry, Dish soap, Salt, Ice-cold Isopropyl alcohol (70% or higher), Zipper-style plastic bag, Coffee filter, Funnel, Wooden coffee stirrer, Clear glass

Week 3	Unit 2 (Honors Course)			5-Day

Weekly Topic

→ This week will wrap up a look at molecular genetics.

	Day 1	Day 2	Day 3	Day 4	Day 5
Textbook and Experiment	❑ Read *CK-12 Biology* Section 7.3.	❑ Read *CK-12 Biology* Section 7.4.	❑ Read the background and procedure sections for the week's lab.	❑ Do the "Build a Gel Electrophoresis Apparatus" lab on pg. 143 in *Illustrated Guide to Home Biology Experiments*.	❑ Do the optional Hands-on Assignment - DNA Extraction.
Writing	❑ Add the vocabulary to the glossary section of your science notebook.	❑ Answer the assigned questions in the reading section of your science notebook.		❑ Record what you have done in the lab section of your science notebook.	
Events in Science	❑ Choose one of the Events in Science assignments to do and add your work to the events section of your science notebook.				

Other Notes

Week 3	Unit 2 (Standard Course)			4-Day
Weekly Topic				
→ This week will wrap up a look at molecular genetics.				
	Day 1	Day 2	Day 3	Day 4
Textbook and Experiment	☐ Read *CK-12 Biology* Section 7.3.	☐ Read *CK-12 Biology* Section 7.4.	☐ Read the background and procedure sections for the week's lab.	☐ Do the "Build a Gel Electrophoresis Apparatus" lab on pg. 143 in *Illustrated Guide to Home Biology Experiments*. **OR** ☐ Do the online lab "Colorblindness Inheritance."
Writing	☐ Add the vocabulary to the glossary section of your science notebook.	☐ Answer the assigned questions in the reading section of your science notebook.		☐ Record what you have done in the lab section of your science notebook.
Other Notes				

Week 3	Unit 2 (Survey Course)	2-Day

Weekly Topic

➔ This week will wrap up a look at molecular genetics.

	Day 1	Day 2
Textbook	❑ Read *CK-12 Biology* Section 7.3.	❑ Read *CK-12 Biology* Section 7.4.
Writing	❑ Add the vocabulary to the glossary section of your science notebook.	❑ Answer the assigned questions in the reading section of your science notebook.
Events in Science	❑ Choose one of the Events in Science assignments to do and add your work to the events section of your science notebook.	

Other Notes

Week 4 Notes - Human Genetics

Textbook Assignments
Reading
📖 *CK-12 Biology* Sections 8.1, 8.2

Written
After you finish reading, answer questions #1-4 in section 8.1 and questions #1-4 in section 8.2. File your work in the reading section of your science notebook. Then, define the following terms in the glossary section of your science notebook:

- ☐ Autosome
- ☐ Human genome
- ☐ Linkage map
- ☐ Sex-linked gene
- ☐ X-linked gene
- ☐ Epistasis
- ☐ Non-disjunction
- ☐ Pleiotrophy

Experiment - Simulated DNA Separation by Gel Electrophoresis
Purpose
The purpose of this lab is to describe the structure and function of DNA, as well as to compare DNA samples for familial and non-familial similarities.

Pre-Reading
✎ Read the background and procedure sections for the "Simulated DNA Separation by Gel Electrophoresis" lab on pg. 149 in *Illustrated Guide to Home Biology Experiments*.

Procedure
✓ Do the lab entitled "Simulated DNA Separation by Gel Electrophoresis" on pg. 149 in *Illustrated Guide to Home Biology Experiments*.

Lab Notebook
☞ Write down on a sheet of paper or type out your notes as you do the experiment. After you are done, print out your lab notes and add them to the lab section of your science notebook.

Lab Questions
✦ Complete the review questions of the "Simulated DNA Separation by Gel Electrophoresis" lab on pg. 154 in *Illustrated Guide to Home Biology Experiments*. Record the answers in the lab section of your science notebook.

Online Lab - Mice Inheritance
Purpose
The purpose of this online lab is to use the virtual Genetics lab to determine the patterns of inheritance of mouse traits.

Pre-Reading
✎ Print and read the section of the workbook for the "Mice Inheritance" online lab.

Procedure
   ✓ Do the lab entitled "Mice Inheritance" and answer the questions as you work through the online lab.

Lab Notebook
   ☞ Add the completed workbook pages that were printed to the lab notebook.

Events in Science

Current Events
   ⏱ Find a current events article relating to the field of genetics and complete the article summary sheet found on pg. 246 of the Appendix. Once you are done, add the sheet to the events section of your science notebook.

Historical Figures
   ⏱ Begin to work on your paper on the life and work of Gregor Mendel. This week, aim to complete your outline and rough draft. See pp. 14-15 for more directions. You will have three weeks to complete this paper.

Hands-on Activity

Optional Hands-on
   ✂ Create a pictorial family tree. Under each picture, note the hair color and eye color of the individual. Then, follow those traits as they are passed down through the family.

Week 4 Supply List

Weekly Experiment	
Supplies from BK01A Biology Kit	☐ Goggles, Agar, Beaker - 250 mL, Graduated cylinder - 100 mL, Glycerol, Pipettes, Reaction plate - 96-well, Ruler, Stain: Hucker's crystal violet, Stain: Methylene blue, Stain: Safranin O, Stirring rod, Thermometer
Additional Supplies From Home	☐ Gel electrophoresis apparatus (from last week), Measuring spoons, Microwave oven, Soda bottle (2 liter, clean and empty), Sodium chloride (table salt), Sodium bicarbonate (baking soda), Toothpicks, Water
Hands-on Activity	
Supplies Needed	☐ Family pictures, Poster board

Week 4	Unit 2 (Honors Course)			5-Day

Weekly Topic

→ This week will look at human genetics.

	Day 1	Day 2	Day 3	Day 4	Day 5
Textbook and Experiment	❑ Read *CK-12 Biology* Section 8.1.	❑ Read *CK-12 Biology* Section 8.2.	❑ Read the background and procedure sections for the week's lab.	❑ Do the "Simulated DNA Separation by Gel Electrophoresis" lab on pg. 149 in *Illustrated Guide to Home Biology Experiments*.	❑ Do the optional Hands-on Assignment - Family Tree.
Writing	❑ Add the vocabulary to the glossary section of your science notebook.	❑ Answer the assigned questions in the reading section of your science notebook.	❑ Take the Chapter 7 Test from *CK-12 Biology*.	❑ Record what you have done in the lab section of your science notebook.	❑ Complete the lab review questions for the week.
Events in Science	❑ Choose one of the Events in Science assignments to do and add your work to the events section of your science notebook.				

Other Notes

Week 4	Unit 2 (Standard Course)	4-Day

Weekly Topic

→ This week will look at human genetics.

	Day 1	Day 2	Day 3	Day 4
Textbook and Experiment	☐ Read *CK-12 Biology* Section 8.1.	☐ Read *CK-12 Biology* Section 8.2.	☐ Read the background and procedure sections for the week's lab.	☐ Do the "Simulated DNA Separation by Gel Electrophoresis" lab on pg. 149 in *Illustrated Guide to Home Biology Experiments*. **OR** ☐ Do the online lab "Mice Inheritance."
Writing	☐ Add the vocabulary to the glossary section of your science notebook.	☐ Answer the assigned questions in the reading section of your science notebook.	☐ Take the Chapter 7 Test from *CK-12 Biology*.	☐ Record what you have done in the lab section of your science notebook.

Other Notes

Week 4	Unit 2 (Survey Course)	2-Day

Weekly Topic

→ This week will look at human genetics.

	Day 1	Day 2
Textbook	❏ Read *CK-12 Biology* Section 8.1.	❏ Read *CK-12 Biology* Section 8.2.
Writing	❏ Add the vocabulary to the glossary section of your science notebook. ❏ Take the Chapter 7 Test from *CK-12 Biology*.	❏ Answer the assigned questions in the reading section of your science notebook.
Events in Science	❏ Choose one of the Events in Science assignments to do and add your work to the events section of your science notebook.	

Other Notes

Week 5 Notes - Biotechnology

Textbook Assignments

Reading
📖 *CK-12 Biology* Section 8.3

Written
After you finish reading, answer questions #1-5 in section 8.3 and file your work in the reading section of your science notebook. Then, define the following terms in the glossary section of your science notebook:

- ☐ Biotechnology
- ☐ Genetic engineering
- ☐ Phramacogenomics
- ☐ Polymerase Chain Reaction (PCR)
- ☐ Transgenic crop

Experiment - Coacervates

Purpose
The purpose of this lab is to practice modern molecular genetic techniques used for bacterial identification.

Pre-Reading
✍ Read the background and procedure sections for the "Coacervates" lab on pg. 131 in *Illustrated Guide to Home Biology Experiments*.

Procedure
✔ Do the lab entitled "Coacervates" on pg. 131 in *Illustrated Guide to Home Biology Experiments*.

Lab Notebook
☞ Write down on a sheet of paper or type out your notes as you do the experiment. After you are done, print out your lab notes and add them to the lab section of your science notebook.

Lab Questions
🖈 Complete the review questions of the "Coacervates" lab on pg. 134 in *Illustrated Guide to Home Biology Experiments*. Record the answers in the lab section of your science notebook.

Online Lab - Sickle Cell Inheritance

Purpose
The purpose of this online lab is to use the virtual Genetics lab to determine the pattern of inheritance of sickle cell disease.

Pre-Reading
✍ Print and read the section of the workbook for the "Sickle Cell Inheritance" online lab.

Procedure
- ✓ Do the lab entitled "Sickle Cell Inheritance" and answer the questions as you work through the online lab.

Lab Notebook
- ☞ Add the completed workbook pages that were printed to the lab notebook.

Events in Science

Current Events
- ☼ Find a current events article relating to the field of biotechnology and complete the article summary sheet found on pg. 246 of the Appendix. Once you are done, add the sheet to the events section of your science notebook.

Historical Figures
- ☼ Continue to work on your paper on the life and work of Gregor Mendel. This week, aim to complete your final draft. See pp. 14-15 for more directions.

Hands-on Activity

Optional Hands-on
- ✄ Learn more about PCR reactions by watching the following 3-D animation: https://www.dnalc.org/resources/3d/19-polymerase-chain-reaction.html.

Week 5 Supply List

Weekly Experiment	
Supplies from BK01A Biology Kit	☐ Goggles, Beaker - 50 mL or 100 mL, Beaker - 250 mL, Centrifuge tube - 15 mL, Centrifuge tubes - 50 mL, Coverslips, Gelatin, Graduated cylinder - 10 mL, Graduated cylinder - 100 mL, Gum arabic, Hydrochloric acid, pH test paper, Pipettes, Reaction plate - 96-well, Slides (flat), Stain: methylene blue, Stain: Sudan III, Test tubes, Thermometer, Spatula, Stirring rod, Stopper (to fit test tube)
Additional Supplies From Home	☐ Gloves, Balance (optional), Microscope, Microwave oven, Water - distilled
Hands-on Activity	
Supplies Needed	☐ None

Week 5	Unit 2 (Honors Course)			5-Day
Weekly Topic				

→ This week will look at biotechnology.

	Day 1	Day 2	Day 3	Day 4	Day 5
Textbook and Experiment	☐ Read *CK-12 Biology* Section 8.3.		☐ Read the background and procedure sections for the week's lab.	☐ Do the "Coacervates" lab on pg. 131 in *Illustrated Guide to Home Biology Experiments*.	☐ Do the optional Hands-on Assignment - PCR Animation.
Writing	☐ Add the vocabulary to the glossary section of your science notebook.	☐ Answer the assigned questions in the reading section of your science notebook.	☐ Take the Chapter 8 Test from *CK-12 Biology*.	☐ Record what you have done in the lab section of your science notebook.	☐ Complete the lab review questions for the week.
Events in Science	☐ Choose one of the Events in Science assignments to do and add your work to the events section of your science notebook.				

Other Notes

Week 5	Unit 2 (Standard Course)		4-Day

Weekly Topic

→ This week will look at biotechnology.

	Day 1	Day 2	Day 3	Day 4
Textbook and Experiment	❑ Read *CK-12 Biology* Section 8.3.		❑ Read the background and procedure sections for the week's lab.	❑ Do the "Coacervates" lab on pg. 131 in *Illustrated Guide to Home Biology Experiments*. **OR** ❑ Do the online lab "Sickle Cell Inheritance."
Writing	❑ Add the vocabulary to the glossary section of your science notebook.	❑ Answer the assigned questions in the reading section of your science notebook.	❑ Take the Chapter 8 Test from *CK-12 Biology*.	❑ Record what you have done in the lab section of your science notebook.

Other Notes

Week 5	Unit 2 (Survey Course)	2-Day

Weekly Topic

→ This week will look at biotechnology.

	Day 1	Day 2
Textbook	❑ Read *CK-12 Biology* Section 8.3.	❑ Take the Chapter 8 Test from *CK-12 Biology*.
Writing	❑ Add the vocabulary to the glossary section of your science notebook.	❑ Answer the assigned questions in the reading section of your science notebook.
Events in Science	❑ Choose one of the Events in Science assignments to do and add your work to the events section of your science notebook.	

Other Notes

Week 6 Notes - Early Organisms

Textbook Assignments

Reading
📖 *CK-12 Biology* Sections 9.1, 9.2, 9.3

Written
After you finish reading, answer questions #1-3 in section 9.1, questions #5-6 in section 9.2, and questions #4-5 in section 9.3. File your work in the reading section of your science notebook. Then, define the following terms in the glossary section of your science notebook:

☐ Extinction	☐ Mesozoic era
☐ Fossil record	☐ Permian extinction
☐ Last Universal Common Ancestor	☐ Clade
☐ Cambrian explosion	☐ Linnean classification system

Experiment - Building and Observing Microcosms

Purpose
The purpose of this lab is to practice building and observing ecosystems.

Pre-Reading
✍ Read the background and procedure sections for the "Building and Observing Microcosms" lab on pg. 79 in *Illustrated Guide to Home Biology Experiments*.

Procedure
✓ Do the lab entitled "Building and Observing Microcosms" on pg. 79 in *Illustrated Guide to Home Biology Experiments*.

Lab Notebook
☞ Write down on a sheet of paper or type out your notes as you do the experiment. After you are done, print out your lab notes and add them to the lab section of your science notebook.

Lab Questions
🕯 Complete the review questions of the "Building and Observing Microcosms" lab on pg. 85 in *Illustrated Guide to Home Biology Experiments*. Record the answers in the lab section of your science notebook.

Online Lab - Gene Linkage in Fruit Flies

Purpose
The purpose of this online lab is to use the virtual Genetics lab to determine how the genes are linked in fruit fly chromosomes.

Pre-Reading
✍ Print and read the section of the workbook for the "Gene Linkage in Fruit Flies" online lab.

Procedure

    ✓ Do the lab entitled "Gene Linkage in Fruit Flies" and answer the questions as you work through the online lab.

Lab Notebook

    ☞ Add the completed workbook pages that were printed to the lab notebook.

Events in Science

Current Events

    🕘 Find a current events article relating to the field of biotechnology and complete the article summary sheet found on pg. 246 of the Appendix. Once you are done, add the sheet to the events section of your science notebook.

Historical Figures

    🕘 There is no historical figures assignment for this week.

Hands-on Activity

Optional Hands-on

    ✂ Complete question #6 (creating your own Linnean classification system) in section 9.3.

Week 6 Supply List

Weekly Experiment	
Supplies from BK01A Biology Kit	❏ Goggles
Additional Supplies From Home	❏ Gloves, Bag - brown paper, Camera (optional), Eggshell and yolk, Funnel (or aluminum foil to make your own), Jars - wide-mouth, Mixing bowl or similar container, Newspaper, Pond water/sediment/vegetation, Shredder and/or scissors, Soft drink bottles - 500 mL or 1 L, Trowel, ladle, or other large scoop, Water
Hands-on Activity	
Supplies Needed	❏ Sheet of paper, Pencil

Week 6	Unit 2 (Honors Course)			5-Day

Weekly Topic

➔ This week will look at early organisms.

	Day 1	Day 2	Day 3	Day 4	Day 5
Textbook and Experiment	❑ Read *CK-12 Biology* Sections 9.1 and 9.2.	❑ Read *CK-12 Biology* Section 9.3.	❑ Read the background and procedure sections for the week's lab.	❑ Do the "Building and Observing Microcosms" lab on pg. 79 in *Illustrated Guide to Home Biology Experiments*.	❑ Do the optional Hands-on Assignment - Linean Classification.
Writing	❑ Add the vocabulary to the glossary section of your science notebook.	❑ Answer the assigned questions in the reading section of your science notebook.		❑ Record what you have done in the lab section of your science notebook.	❑ Complete the lab review questions for the week.
Events in Science	❑ Choose one of the Events in Science assignments to do and add your work to the events section of your science notebook.				

Other Notes

Week 6	Unit 2 (Standard Course)		4-Day

Weekly Topic

→ This week will look at early organisms.

	Day 1	Day 2	Day 3	Day 4
Textbook and Experiment	❏ Read *CK-12 Biology* Sections 9.1 and 9.2.	❏ Read *CK-12 Biology* Section 9.3.	❏ Read the background and procedure sections for the week's lab.	❏ Do the "Building and Observing Microcosms" lab on pg. 79 in *Illustrated Guide to Home Biology Experiments*. **OR** ❏ Do the online lab "Gene Linkage in Fruit Flies."
Writing	❏ Add the vocabulary to the glossary section of your science notebook.	❏ Answer the assigned questions in the reading section of your science notebook.		❏ Record what you have done in the lab section of your science notebook.

Other Notes

Week 6	Unit 2 (Survey Course)	2-Day

Weekly Topic

→ This week will look at early organisms.

	Day 1	Day 2
Textbook	☐ Read *CK-12 Biology* Sections 9.1 and 9.2.	☐ Read *CK-12 Biology* Section 9.3.
Writing	☐ Add the vocabulary to the glossary section of your science notebook.	☐ Answer the assigned questions in the reading section of your science notebook.
Events in Science	☐ Choose one of the Events in Science assignments to do and add your work to the events section of your science notebook.	

Other Notes

Week 7 Notes - Theory of Evolution

Textbook Assignments
Reading
 📖 *CK-12 Biology* Sections 10.1, 10.2, 10.3, 10.4
Written
 After you finish reading, answer questions #1-7 in section 10.1 and #1-5 in 10.2 and file your work in the reading section of your science notebook. Then, define the following terms in the glossary section of your science notebook:

- ☐ Artificial selection
- ☐ Fitness
- ☐ Adaptive radiation
- ☐ Biogeography
- ☐ Homologous structure
- ☐ Vestigial structure
- ☐ Allele frequency
- ☐ Hardy-Weinberg theorem
- ☐ Macroevolution
- ☐ Microevolution
- ☐ Coevolution
- ☐ Speciation

Experiment - Observing Succession in Aquarium Microcosms
Purpose
 The purpose of this lab is to observe succession in contained aquatic ecosystems.
Pre-Reading
 ✍ Read the background and procedure sections for the "Observing Succession in Aquarium Microcosms" lab on pg. 87 in *Illustrated Guide to Home Biology Experiments*.
Procedure
 ✓ Do the lab entitled "Observing Succession in Aquarium Microcosms" on pg. 87 in *Illustrated Guide to Home Biology Experiments*.
Lab Notebook
 ☞ Write down on a sheet of paper or type out your notes as you do the experiment. After you are done, print out your lab notes and add them to the lab section of your science notebook.
Lab Questions
 🌢 Complete the review questions of the "Observing Succession in Aquarium Microcosms" lab on pg. 90 in *Illustrated Guide to Home Biology Experiments*. Record the answers in the lab section of your science notebook.

Online Lab - Introduction to the Systematics Lab
Purpose
 The purpose of this online lab is to discover how scientists classify species according to their evolutionary history.

Pre-Reading

   ↶ Print and read the section of the workbook for the "Introduction to the Systematics Lab" online lab.

Procedure

   ✓ Do the lab entitled "Introduction to the Systematics Lab" and answer the questions as you work through the online lab.

Lab Notebook

   ☞ Add the completed workbook pages that were printed to the lab notebook.

Events in Science

Current Events

   ⊕ Find a current events article relating to the field of biotechnology and complete the article summary sheet found on pg. 246 of the Appendix. Once you are done, add the sheet to the events section of your science notebook.

Historical Figures

   ⊕ There is no historical figures assignment for this week.

Hands-on Activity

Optional Hands-on

   ✂ There is no optional hands-on activity for this week.

Week 7 Supply List

Weekly Experiment	
Supplies from BK01A Biology Kit	☐ Goggles, Coverslips, Methylcellulose, pH test paper, Pipettes, Slides - flat, Stain: eosin Y, Stain: methylene blue, Thermometer
Additional Supplies From Home	☐ Gloves, Aquarium microcosms (from preceding lab), Particulate masks N100, Watch or clock with second hand
Hands-on Activity	
Supplies Needed	☐ None

Week 7	Unit 2 (Honors Course)			5-Day

Weekly Topic

→ This week will look at the theory of evolution.

	Day 1	Day 2	Day 3	Day 4	Day 5
Textbook and Experiment	❏ Read *CK-12 Biology* Sections 10.1 and 10.2.	❏ Read *CK-12 Biology* Sections 10.3 and 10.4.	❏ Read the background and procedure sections for the week's lab.	❏ Do the "Observing Succession in Aquarium Microcosms" lab on pg. 87 in *Illustrated Guide to Home Biology Experiments*.	
Writing	❏ Add the vocabulary to the glossary section of your science notebook.	❏ Answer the assigned questions in the reading section of your science notebook.	❏ Take the Chapter 9 Test from *CK-12 Biology*.	❏ Record what you have done in the lab section of your science notebook.	❏ Complete the lab review questions for the week.
Events in Science	❏ Choose one of the Events in Science assignments to do and add your work to the events section of your science notebook.				

Other Notes

Week 7	Unit 2 (Standard Course)			4-Day

Weekly Topic

→ This week will look at the theory of evolution.

	Day 1	Day 2	Day 3	Day 4
Textbook and Experiment	❑ Read *CK-12 Biology* Sections 10.1 and 10.2.	❑ Read *CK-12 Biology* Sections 10.3 and 10.4.	❑ Read the background and procedure sections for the week's lab.	❑ Do the "Observing Succession in Aquarium Microcosms" lab on pg. 87 in *Illustrated Guide to Home Biology Experiments*. **OR** ❑ Do the online lab "Introduction to the Systematics Lab."
Writing	❑ Add the vocabulary to the glossary section of your science notebook.	❑ Answer the assigned questions in the reading section of your science notebook.	❑ Take the Chapter 9 Test from *CK-12 Biology*.	❑ Record what you have done in the lab section of your science notebook.

Other Notes

Week 7	Unit 2 (Survey Course)	2-Day

Weekly Topic

→ This week will look at the theory of evolution.

	Day 1	Day 2
Textbook	❑ Read *CK-12 Biology* Sections 10.1 and 10.2.	❑ Read *CK-12 Biology* Sections 10.3 and 10.4.
Writing	❑ Add the vocabulary to the glossary section of your science notebook. ❑ Take the Chapter 9 Test from *CK-12 Biology*.	❑ Answer the assigned questions in the reading section of your science notebook.
Events in Science	❑ Choose one of the Events in Science assignments to do and add your work to the events section of your science notebook.	

Other Notes

Biology for High School

Unit 3 - Ecology, Eukaryotes, and Plant Life

Week 1 Notes - Principles of Ecology

Textbook Assignments

Reading

📖 *CK-12 Biology* Sections 11.1, 11.2, 11.3

Written

After you finish reading, answer questions #1-5 in section 11.1, questions #1-3 in section 11.2, and questions #1-3 in section 11.3. File your work in the reading section of your science notebook. Then, define the following terms in the glossary section of your science notebook:

- ☐ Abiotic factor
- ☐ Biotic factor
- ☐ Chemoautotroph
- ☐ Detritivore
- ☐ Photoautotroph
- ☐ Saprotroph
- ☐ Biogeochemical cycle
- ☐ Exchange pool
- ☐ Aphotic zone
- ☐ Intertidal zone
- ☐ Photic zone

Experiment - Observing the Effects of Pollution in Microcosms

Purpose

The purpose of this lab is to observe the effects of pollution in microcosms.

Pre-Reading

✍ Read the background and procedure sections for the "Observing the Effects of Pollution in Microcosms" lab on pg. 93 in *Illustrated Guide to Home Biology Experiments*.

Procedure

✓ Do the lab entitled "Observing the Effects of Pollution in Microcosms" on pg. 93 in *Illustrated Guide to Home Biology Experiments*.

Lab Notebook

☞ Write down on a sheet of paper or type out your notes as you do the experiment. After you are done, print out your lab notes and add them to the lab section of your science notebook.

Lab Questions

🖊 Complete the review questions of the "Observing the Effects of Pollution in Microcosms" lab on pg. 96 in *Illustrated Guide to Home Biology Experiments*. Record the answers in the lab section of your science notebook.

Online Lab

☞ There is no online lab scheduled for this week.

Events in Science

Current Events

🕐 Find a current events article relating to the field of ecology and complete the article summary sheet found on pg. 246 of the Appendix. Once you are done, add the sheet to the events section of your science notebook.

Historical Figures

🕐 Begin to research the life and work of Alexander von Humboldt, who is considered by many to be the father of modern ecology. You will have three weeks to complete your research. After that, you will have two weeks to prepare a two to three page paper on this scientist and his contributions to the field of biology.

Hands-on Activity

Optional Hands-on

✂ Observe the ecosystem in which you live. You can do this from your backyard or from a local trail. Be sure to look for both abiotic and biotic factors. Afterword, create a journal page detailing what you have observed.

Week 1 Supply List

Weekly Experiment	
Supplies from BK01A Biology Kit	☐ Goggles, Coverslips, Centrifuge tubes - 50 mL, Hydrochloric acid, Fertilizer concentrate A, Lead(II) acetate, Methylcellulose, pH test paper, Pipettes, Slides - flat, Yeast, live (baker's or brewer's)
Additional Supplies From Home	☐ Gloves, Foam cup, Pond sediment/vegetation, Tablespoon, Water
Hands-on Activity	
Supplies Needed	☐ Sheet of paper, Pencil

Week 1	Unit 3 (Honors Course)			5-Day

Weekly Topic				
→ This week will look at the principles of ecology.				

	Day 1	Day 2	Day 3	Day 4	Day 5
Textbook and Experiment	❐ Read *CK-12 Biology* Sections 11.1 and 11.2.	❐ Read *CK-12 Biology* Section 11.3.	❐ Read the background and procedure sections for the week's lab.	❐ Do the "Observing the Effects of Pollution in Microcosms" lab on pg. 93 in *Illustrated Guide to Home Biology Experiments*.	❐ Do the optional Hands-on Assignment - Ecosystem Observation.
Writing	❐ Add the vocabulary to the glossary section of your science notebook.	❐ Answer the assigned questions in the reading section of your science notebook.	❐ Take the Chapter 10 Test from *CK-12 Biology*.	❐ Record what you have done in the lab section of your science notebook.	❐ Complete the lab review questions for the week.
Events in Science	❐ Choose one of the Events in Science assignments to do and add your work to the events section of your science notebook.				

Other Notes

Week 1	Unit 3 (Standard Course)		4-Day

Weekly Topic

→ This week will look at the principles of ecology.

	Day 1	Day 2	Day 3	Day 4
Textbook and Experiment	☐ Read *CK-12 Biology* Sections 11.1 and 11.2.	☐ Read *CK-12 Biology* Section 11.3.	☐ Read the background and procedure sections for the week's lab.	☐ Do the "Observing the Effects of Pollution in Microcosms" lab on pg. 93 in *Illustrated Guide to Home Biology Experiments*.
Writing	☐ Add the vocabulary to the glossary section of your science notebook.	☐ Answer the assigned questions in the reading section of your science notebook.	☐ Take the Chapter 10 Test from *CK-12 Biology*.	☐ Record what you have done in the lab section of your science notebook.

Other Notes

Week 1	Unit 3 (Survey Course)	2-Day

Weekly Topic

→ This week will look at the principles of ecology.

	Day 1	Day 2
Textbook	❐ Read *CK-12 Biology* Sections 11.1 and 11.2.	❐ Read *CK-12 Biology* Section 11.3.
Writing	❐ Add the vocabulary to the glossary section of your science notebook. ❐ Take the Chapter 10 Test from *CK-12 Biology*.	❐ Answer the assigned questions in the reading section of your science notebook.
Events in Science	❐ Choose one of the Events in Science assignments to do and add your work to the events section of your science notebook.	

Other Notes

Week 2 Notes - Communities and Populations, part 1

Textbook Assignments
Reading
📖 *CK-12 Biology* Sections 12.1, 12.2

Written
After you finish reading, answer questions #1-3 in section 12.1 and questions #1-5 in section 12.2. File your work in the reading section of your science notebook. Then, define the following terms in the glossary section of your science notebook:

- ☐ Commensalism
- ☐ Keystone species
- ☐ Mutualism
- ☐ Primary succession
- ☐ Secondary succession
- ☐ Carrying capacity
- ☐ Dispersal
- ☐ *r*-selected

Experiment - Sampling Plant Populations in a Community
Purpose
The purpose of this lab is to learn how to sample plant populations in a community.

Pre-Reading
✐ Read the background and procedure sections for the "Sampling Plant Populations in a Community" lab on pg. 185 in *Illustrated Guide to Home Biology Experiments*.

Procedure
✓ Do the lab entitled "Sampling Plant Populations in a Community" on pg. 185 in *Illustrated Guide to Home Biology Experiments*.

Lab Notebook
☞ Write down on a sheet of paper or type out your notes as you do the experiment. After you are done, print out your lab notes and add them to the lab section of your science notebook.

Lab Questions
🐾 Complete the review questions of the "Sampling Plant Populations in a Community" lab on pg. 191 in *Illustrated Guide to Home Biology Experiments*. Record the answers in the lab section of your science notebook.

Online Lab - Introduction to Ecology
Purpose
The purpose of this online lab is to familiarize yourself with the virtual Ecology lab bench and its simulations.

Pre-Reading
✐ Print and read the section of the workbook for the "Introduction to Ecology" online lab.

Procedure
    ✓ Do the lab entitled "Introduction to Ecology" and answer the questions as you work through the online lab.

Lab Notebook
    ☞ Add the completed workbook pages that were printed to the lab notebook.

Events in Science
Current Events
    🕐 Find a current events article relating to the field of ecology and complete the article summary sheet found on pg. 246 of the Appendix. Once you are done, add the sheet to the events section of your science notebook.

Historical Figures
    🕐 Continue to research the life and work of Alexander von Humboldt.

Hands-on Activity
Optional Hands-on
    ✂ Research the abiotic factors and resources that are found in your community.

Week 2 Supply List

Weekly Experiment	
Supplies from BK01A Biology Kit	☐ Centrifuge tubes (specimen containers), Magnifier, Ruler
Additional Supplies From Home	☐ Gloves, Assistant, Camera (optional, with macro feature), Hammer or mallet, Marking pen (for labeling), Field guides to plants and trees (for your region), Plastic bags (specimen containers), Pocket knife, Scissors, Stakes, String or cord (250 feet or 75 meters), Tape measure (50-foot or 15-meter)
Hands-on Activity	
Supplies Needed	

Week 2	Unit 3 (Honors Course)			5-Day

Weekly Topic

→ This week will begin a look at communities and populations.

	Day 1	Day 2	Day 3	Day 4	Day 5
Textbook and Experiment	☐ Read *CK-12 Biology* Section 12.1.	☐ Read *CK-12 Biology* Section 12.2.	☐ Read the background and procedure sections for the week's lab.	☐ Do the "Sampling Plant Populations in a Community" lab on pg. 185 in *Illustrated Guide to Home Biology Experiments*.	☐ Do the optional Hands-on Assignment - Abiotic Factors.
Writing	☐ Add the vocabulary to the glossary section of your science notebook.	☐ Answer the assigned questions in the reading section of your science notebook.	☐ Take the Chapter 11 Test from *CK-12 Biology*.	☐ Record what you have done in the lab section of your science notebook.	☐ Complete the lab review questions for the week.
Events in Science	☐ Choose one of the Events in Science assignments to do and add your work to the events section of your science notebook.				

Other Notes

Week 2	Unit 3 (Standard Course)		4-Day

Weekly Topic

→ This week will begin a look at communities and populations.

	Day 1	Day 2	Day 3	Day 4
Textbook and Experiment	❑ Read *CK-12 Biology* Section 12.1.	❑ Read *CK-12 Biology* Sections 12.2.	❑ Read the background and procedure sections for the week's lab.	❑ Do the "Sampling Plant Populations in a Community" lab on pg. 185 in *Illustrated Guide to Home Biology Experiments*. **OR** ❑ Do the online lab "Introduction to Ecology."
Writing	❑ Add the vocabulary to the glossary section of your science notebook.	❑ Answer the assigned questions in the reading section of your science notebook.	❑ Take the Chapter 11 Test from *CK-12 Biology*.	❑ Record what you have done in the lab section of your science notebook.

Other Notes

Week 2	Unit 3 (Survey Course)	2-Day

Weekly Topic

→ This week will begin a look at communities and populations.

	Day 1	Day 2
Textbook	❏ Read *CK-12 Biology* Section 12.1.	❏ Read *CK-12 Biology* Sections 12.2.
Writing	❏ Add the vocabulary to the glossary section of your science notebook. ❏ Take the Chapter 11 Test from *CK-12 Biology*.	❏ Answer the assigned questions in the reading section of your science notebook.
Events in Science	❏ Choose one of the Events in Science assignments to do and add your work to the events section of your science notebook.	

Other Notes

Week 3 Notes - Communities and Populations, part 2

Textbook Assignments
Reading
📖 *CK-12 Biology* Sections 12.3, 12.4, 12.5

Written
After you finish reading, answer questions #1-3 in section 12.3, questions #1-4 in section 12.4, and questions #1-4 in section 12.5. File your work in the reading section of your science notebook. Then, define the following terms in the glossary section of your science notebook:

- ☐ Demographic transition
- ☐ Sixth mass extinction
- ☐ Algal bloom
- ☐ Ozone hole

Experiment - Observe the Effects of Rhizobia on Plant Growth
Purpose
The purpose of this lab is to study the effects of rhizobs on plant growth and their impacts on plant production.

Pre-Reading
✍ Read the background and procedure sections for the "Observe the Effects of Rhizobia on Plant Growth" lab on pg. 193 in *Illustrated Guide to Home Biology Experiments*.

Procedure
✓ Do the lab entitled "Observe the Effects of Rhizobia on Plant Growth" on pg. 193 in *Illustrated Guide to Home Biology Experiments*.

Lab Notebook
☞ Write down on a sheet of paper or type out your notes as you do the experiment. After you are done, print out your lab notes and add them to the lab section of your science notebook.

Lab Questions
🌢 Complete the review questions of the "Observe the Effects of Rhizobia on Plant Growth" lab on pg. 197 in *Illustrated Guide to Home Biology Experiments*. Record the answers in the lab section of your science notebook.

Online Lab - Invasive Species
Purpose
The purpose of this online lab is to determine the effect an invasive species can have on an ecosystem.

Pre-Reading
✍ Print and read the section of the workbook for the "Invasive Species" online lab.

Procedure
> ✓ Do the lab entitled "Invasive Species" and answer the questions as you work through the online lab.

Lab Notebook
> ☞ Add the completed workbook pages that were printed to the lab notebook.

Events in Science

Current Events
> ⊕ Find a current events article relating to the field of ecology and complete the article summary sheet found on pg. 246 of the Appendix. Once you are done, add the sheet to the events section of your science notebook.

Historical Figures
> ⊕ Continue to research the life and work of Alexander von Humboldt.

Hands-on Activity

Optional Hands-on
> ✂ This week, draw a food web for your community using the five animals you chose from the previous week and several of the plants they feed on. Be sure to label them with their appropriate trophic levels (e.g., primary producer, primary consumer, and so on).

Week 3 Supply List

Weekly Experiment	
Supplies from BK01A Biology Kit	☐ Ammonium nitrate, Fertilizer, nitrogen-free (concentrate A), Fertilizer, nitrogen-free (concentrate B), Fertilizer, nitrogen-free (concentrate C), Graduated cylinder - 10 mL, Inoculating loop, Rhizobia inoculum, Ruler, Seeds - bush lima bean
Additional Supplies From Home	☐ Gloves, Balance, Chlorine laundry bleach, Foam cups, 16 oz./500 mL, Lamp, fluorescent plant (optional), Paper towel, Pencil, Plastic wrap (Saran or similar), Soft drink bottle - 2-liter, Vermiculite (or other sterile growth medium), Water - distilled
Hands-on Activity	
Supplies Needed	☐ Sheet of paper, Pencil

Week 3	Unit 3 (Honors Course)			5-Day

Weekly Topic

→ This week will wrap up a look at communities and populations.

	Day 1	Day 2	Day 3	Day 4	Day 5
Textbook and Experiment	❑ Read *CK-12 Biology* Sections 12.3 and 12.4.	❑ Read *CK-12 Biology* Section 12.5.	❑ Read the background and procedure sections for the week's lab.	❑ Do the "Observe the Effects of Rhizobia on Plant Growth" lab on pg. 193 in *Illustrated Guide to Home Biology Experiments*.	❑ Do the optional Hands-on Assignment - Food Web.
Writing	❑ Add the vocabulary to the glossary section of your science notebook.	❑ Answer the assigned questions in the reading section of your science notebook.		❑ Record what you have done in the lab section of your science notebook.	❑ Complete the lab review questions for the week.
Events in Science	❑ Choose one of the Events in Science assignments to do and add your work to the events section of your science notebook.				

Other Notes

Week 3	Unit 3 (Standard Course)		4-Day

Weekly Topic

→ This week will wrap up a look at communities and populations.

	Day 1	Day 2	Day 3	Day 4
Textbook and Experiment	❏ Read *CK-12 Biology* Sections 12.3 and 12.4.	❏ Read *CK-12 Biology* Sections 12.5.	❏ Read the background and procedure sections for the week's lab.	❏ Do the "Observe the Effects of Rhizobia on Plant Growth" lab on pg. 193 in *Illustrated Guide to Home Biology Experiments*. **OR** ❏ Do the online lab "Invasive Species."
Writing	❏ Add the vocabulary to the glossary section of your science notebook.	❏ Answer the assigned questions in the reading section of your science notebook.		❏ Record what you have done in the lab section of your science notebook.

Other Notes

Week 3	Unit 3 (Survey Course)	2-Day

Weekly Topic

➔ This week will wrap up a look at communities and populations.

	Day 1	Day 2
Textbook	☐ Read *CK-12 Biology* Sections 12.1.	☐ Read *CK-12 Biology* Sections 12.2.
Writing	☐ Add the vocabulary to the glossary section of your science notebook.	☐ Answer the assigned questions in the reading section of your science notebook.
Events in Science	☐ Choose one of the Events in Science assignments to do and add your work to the events section of your science notebook.	

Other Notes

Week 4 Notes - Microorganisms

Textbook Assignments
Reading
📖 *CK-12 Biology* Sections 13.1, 13.2
Written
After you finish reading, answer questions #1-5 in section 13.1 and questions #1-5 in section 13.2. File your work in the reading section of your science notebook. Then, define the following terms in the glossary section of your science notebook:

- Archaea
- Biofilm
- Cyanobacteria
- Extremophile
- Plasmid
- Vector
- Capsid
- Latency
- Vaccine
- Virion

Experiment - Air Pollution Testing
Purpose
The purpose of this lab is to test for air pollution.
Pre-Reading
✍ Read the background and procedure sections for the "Air Pollution Testing" lab on pg. 199 in *Illustrated Guide to Home Biology Experiments*.
Procedure
✓ Do the lab entitled "Air Pollution Testing" on pg. 199 in *Illustrated Guide to Home Biology Experiments*.
Lab Notebook
☞ Write down on a sheet of paper or type out your notes as you do the experiment. After you are done, print out your lab notes and add them to the lab section of your science notebook.
Lab Questions
🐾 Complete the review questions of the "Air Pollution Testing" lab on pg. 203 in *Illustrated Guide to Home Biology Experiments*. Record the answers in the lab section of your science notebook.

Online Lab - Keystone Species
Purpose
The purpose of this online lab is to see how the removal of predators can disrupt food webs.
Pre-Reading
✍ Print and read the section of the workbook for the "Keystone Species" online lab.

Procedure
  ✓ Do the lab entitled "Keystone Species" and answer the questions as you work through the online lab.

Lab Notebook
  ☞ Add the completed workbook pages that were printed to the lab notebook.

Events in Science

Current Events
  ⏰ Find a current events article relating to the field of microbiology and complete the article summary sheet found on pg. 246 of the Appendix. Once you are done, add the sheet to the events section of your science notebook.

Historical Figures
  ⏰ Begin to work on your paper on the life and work of Alexander von Humboldt. This week, aim to complete your outline and rough draft. See pp. 14-15 for more directions. You will have three weeks to complete this paper.

Hands-on Activity

Optional Hands-on
  ✂ There is no optional hands-on activity for this week.

Week 4 Supply List

Weekly Experiment	
Supplies from BK01A Biology Kit	❏ Microscope Slides
Additional Supplies From Home	❏ Gloves, Saucers or similar containers, Microscope, Petroleum jelly, Plastic wrap (Saran or similar), Spray bottle (optional), Watch or timer
Hands-on Activity	
Supplies Needed	❏ None

Week 4	Unit 3 (Honors Course)			5-Day

Weekly Topic

→ This week will look at microorganisms.

	Day 1	Day 2	Day 3	Day 4	Day 5
Textbook and Experiment	❏ Read *CK-12 Biology* Section 13.1.	❏ Read *CK-12 Biology* Section 13.2.	❏ Read the background and procedure sections for the week's lab.	❏ Do the "Air Pollution Testing" lab on pg. 199 in *Illustrated Guide to Home Biology Experiments*.	
Writing	❏ Add the vocabulary to the glossary section of your science notebook.	❏ Answer the assigned questions in the reading section of your science notebook.	❏ Take the Chapter 12 Test from *CK-12 Biology*.	❏ Record what you have done in the lab section of your science notebook.	❏ Complete the lab review questions for the week.
Events in Science	❏ Choose one of the Events in Science assignments to do and add your work to the events section of your science notebook.				

Other Notes

Week 4	Unit 3 (Standard Course)		4-Day

Weekly Topic

➔ This week will look at microorganisms.

	Day 1	Day 2	Day 3	Day 4
Textbook and Experiment	❏ Read *CK-12 Biology* Section 13.1.	❏ Read *CK-12 Biology* Section 13.2.	❏ Read the background and procedure sections for the week's lab.	❏ Do the "Air Pollution Testing" lab on pg. 199 in *Illustrated Guide to Home Biology Experiments*. **OR** ❏ Do the online lab "Keystone Species."
Writing	❏ Add the vocabulary to the glossary section of your science notebook.	❏ Answer the assigned questions in the reading section of your science notebook.	❏ Take the Chapter 12 Test from *CK-12 Biology*.	❏ Record what you have done in the lab section of your science notebook.

Other Notes

Week 4	Unit 3 (Survey Course)	2-Day

Weekly Topic
→ This week will look at microorganisms.

	Day 1	Day 2
Textbook	❑ Read *CK-12 Biology* Section 13.1.	❑ Read *CK-12 Biology* Section 13.2.
Writing	❑ Add the vocabulary to the glossary section of your science notebook. ❑ Take the Chapter 12 Test from *CK-12 Biology*.	❑ Answer the assigned questions in the reading section of your science notebook.
Events in Science	❑ Choose one of the Events in Science assignments to do and add your work to the events section of your science notebook.	

Other Notes

Week 5 Notes - Eukaryotes, part 1

Textbook Assignments
Reading
📖 *CK-12 Biology* Sections 14.1, 14.2, 14.3

Written
After you finish reading, answer questions #1-3 in section 14.1, questions #1-3 in section 14.2, and questions #3, 4 in section 14.3. File your work in the reading section of your science notebook. Then, define the following terms in the glossary section of your science notebook:

- ☐ Cilia
- ☐ Motility
- ☐ Protist
- ☐ Pseudopod
- ☐ Amoeboid
- ☐ Flagellate
- ☐ Protozoa

- ☐ Slime mold
- ☐ Sporozoa
- ☐ Budding
- ☐ Chitin
- ☐ Hyphae
- ☐ Mycelium
- ☐ Zygospore

Experiment - Soil and Water Pollution Testing
Purpose
The purpose of this lab is to learn how to conduct soil and water pollution testing in various water and soil samples.

Pre-Reading
✍ Read the background and procedure sections for the "Soil and Water Pollution Testing" lab on pg. 205 in *Illustrated Guide to Home Biology Experiments*.

Procedure
✓ Do the lab entitled "Soil and Water Pollution Testing" on pg. 205 in *Illustrated Guide to Home Biology Experiments*.

Lab Notebook
☞ Write down on a sheet of paper or type out your notes as you do the experiment. After you are done, print out your lab notes and add them to the lab section of your science notebook.

Lab Questions
🔖 Complete the review questions of the "Soil and Water Pollution Testing" lab on pg. 210 in *Illustrated Guide to Home Biology Experiments*. Record the answers in the lab section of your science notebook.

Online Lab - Predator Competition
Purpose
The purpose of this online lab is to see how the removal of a predator can affect competition at lower trophic levels.

Pre-Reading
 ᕽ Print and read the section of the workbook for the "Predator Competition" online lab.

Procedure
 ✓ Do the lab entitled "Predator Competition" and answer the questions as you work through the online lab.

Lab Notebook
 ☞ Add the completed workbook pages that were printed to the lab notebook.

Events in Science

Current Events
 ☕ Find a current events article relating to the field of microbiology and complete the article summary sheet found on pg. 246 of the Appendix. Once you are done, add the sheet to the events section of your science notebook.

Historical Figures
 ☕ Continue to work on your paper on the life and work of Alexander von Humboldt. This week, aim to complete your final draft. See pp. 14-15 for more directions.

Hands-on Activity

Optional Hands-on
 ✂ Look for a mushroom outside. Then, with gloves on, remove the mushroom for observation and dig below it to look for mycelium to observe. Use a magnifying glass or hand-held microscope (a.k.a. jeweler's scope) to look closer at the structures of a fungus.

Week 5 Supply List

Weekly Experiment	
Supplies from BK01A Biology Kit	☐ Goggles, Centrifuge tubes, Hydrochloric acid, Pipettes, Reaction plate - 24-well, Sodium borate solution - 0.1% w/r to boron, Turmeric reagent
Additional Supplies From Home	☐ Gloves, Desk lamp or other strong light source, Paper towels, Specimens (see text), Water - distilled
Hands-on Activity	
Supplies Needed	☐ Gloves, Trowel, Magnifying glass or hand-held microscope

Week 5	Unit 3 (Honors Course)			5-Day

Weekly Topic

→ This week will begin a look at eukaryotes.

	Day 1	Day 2	Day 3	Day 4	Day 5
Textbook and Experiment	❑ Read *CK-12 Biology* Sections 14.1 and 14.2.	❑ Read *CK-12 Biology* Section 14.3.	❑ Read the background and procedure sections for the week's lab.	❑ Do the "Soil and Water Pollution Testing" lab on pg. 205 in *Illustrated Guide to Home Biology Experiments*.	❑ Do the optional Hands-on Assignment - Mushroom Investigation.
Writing	❑ Add the vocabulary to the glossary section of your science notebook.	❑ Answer the assigned questions in the reading section of your science notebook.	❑ Take the Chapter 13 Test from *CK-12 Biology*.	❑ Record what you have done in the lab section of your science notebook.	❑ Complete the lab review questions for the week.
Events in Science	❑ Choose one of the Events in Science assignments to do and add your work to the events section of your science notebook.				

Other Notes

Week 5	Unit 3 (Standard Course)		4-Day

Weekly Topic

→ This week will begin a look at eukaryotes.

	Day 1	Day 2	Day 3	Day 4
Textbook and Experiment	❏ Read *CK-12 Biology* Sections 14.1 and 14.2.	❏ Read *CK-12 Biology* Section 14.3.	❏ Read the background and procedure sections for the week's lab.	❏ Do the "Soil and Water Pollution Testing" lab on pg. 205 in *Illustrated Guide to Home Biology Experiments*. **OR** ❏ Do the online lab "Predator Competition."
Writing	❏ Add the vocabulary to the glossary section of your science notebook.	❏ Answer the assigned questions in the reading section of your science notebook.	❏ Take the Chapter 13 Test from *CK-12 Biology*.	❏ Record what you have done in the lab section of your science notebook.

Other Notes

Week 5	Unit 3 (Survey Course)	2-Day

Weekly Topic

→ This week will begin a look at eukaryotes.

	Day 1	Day 2
Textbook	❑ Read *CK-12 Biology* Sections 14.1 and 14.2.	❑ Read *CK-12 Biology* Section 14.3.
Writing	❑ Add the vocabulary to the glossary section of your science notebook. ❑ Take the Chapter 13 Test from *CK-12 Biology*.	❑ Answer the assigned questions in the reading section of your science notebook.
Events in Science	❑ Choose one of the Events in Science assignments to do and add your work to the events section of your science notebook.	

Other Notes

Week 6 Notes - Eukaryotes, part 2

Textbook Assignments
Reading
 📖 *CK-12 Biology* Sections 14. 4, 14.5

Written
   After you finish reading, answer questions #1-4 in section 14.4 and questions #1-4 in 14.5. File your work in the reading section of your science notebook. Then, define the following terms in the glossary section of your science notebook:

☐ Lichen	☐ Giardiasis
☐ Mycorrhiza	☐ Malaria
☐ Candidiasis	☐ Ringworm

Experiment - Preparing Culturing Media
Purpose
   The purpose of this lab is to learn how to prepare culture media to grow various bacteria in culture.

Pre-Reading
  ✍ Read the background and procedure sections for the "Preparing Culture Media" lab on pg. 223 in *Illustrated Guide to Home Biology Experiments*.

Procedure
  ✓ Do the lab entitled "Preparing Culture Media" on pg. 223 in *Illustrated Guide to Home Biology Experiments*.

Lab Notebook
  ☞ Write down on a sheet of paper or type out your notes as you do the experiment. After you are done, print out your lab notes and add them to the lab section of your science notebook.

Lab Questions
  🔖 Complete the review questions of the "Preparing Culture Media" lab on pg. 229 in *Illustrated Guide to Home Biology Experiments*. Record the answers in the lab section of your science notebook.

Online Lab - Land Plants
Purpose
   The purpose of this online lab is to learn the major trends in land plant evolution, and how different groups of land plants are related.

Pre-Reading
  ✍ Print and read the section of the workbook for the "Land Plants" online lab.

Procedure

✓ Do the lab entitled "Land Plants" and answer the questions as you work through the online lab.

Lab Notebook

☞ Add the completed workbook pages that were printed to the lab notebook.

Events in Science

Current Events

🕐 Find a current events article relating to the field of microbiology and complete the article summary sheet found on pg. 246 of the Appendix. Once you are done, add the sheet to the events section of your science notebook.

Historical Figures

🕐 Begin to research the life and work of Carl Linnaeus, who is considered by many to be the father of modern biological classification systems. You will have two weeks to complete your research. After that, you will have two weeks to prepare a two to three page paper on this scientist and his contributions to the field of biology.

Hands-on Activity

Optional Hands-on

✂ Study the different types of lichens. Directions for this project can be found here: http://elementalblogging.com/homeschool-science-lichens/.

Week 6 Supply List

Weekly Experiment	
Supplies from BK01A Biology Kit	☐ Goggles, Agar, Bottle (polypropylene, 125 mL), Centrifuge tubes - 15 mL, Petri dishes, Spatula, Stirring rod, Test tubes, Test tube rack, Thermometer
Additional Supplies From Home	☐ Gloves, Aluminum foil, Balance (or measuring spoons), Bottle - 500 mL soda, Broth, chicken (or bouillon cube), Cotton balls, Marking pen, Measuring cup -500 mL, Microwave oven, Pressure cooker (optional; see text), Refrigerator, Sodium chloride (table salt), Spray disinfectant (Lysol or similar), Sprayer bottle filled with water, Sucrose (table sugar), Tape, Water - distilled
Hands-on Activity	
Supplies Needed	☐ Magnifying glass or hand-held microscope, Putty knife

Week 6		Unit 3 (Honors Course)			5-Day

Weekly Topic

➜ This week will wrap up a look at eukaryotes.

	Day 1	Day 2	Day 3	Day 4	Day 5
Textbook and Experiment	❏ Read *CK-12 Biology* Section 14.4.	❏ Read *CK-12 Biology* Section 14.5.	❏ Read the background and procedure sections for the week's lab.	❏ Do the "Preparing Culture Media" lab on pg. 223 in *Illustrated Guide to Home Biology Experiments*.	❏ Do the optional Hands-on Assignment - Lichens.
Writing	❏ Add the vocabulary to the glossary section of your science notebook.	❏ Answer the assigned questions in the reading section of your science notebook.		❏ Record what you have done in the lab section of your science notebook.	❏ Complete the lab review questions for the week.
Events in Science	❏ Choose one of the Events in Science assignments to do and add your work to the events section of your science notebook.				

Other Notes

Week 6	Unit 3 (Standard Course)			4-Day
Weekly Topic				
➔ This week will wrap up a look at eukaryotes.				
	Day 1	Day 2	Day 3	Day 4
Textbook and Experiment	❏ Read *CK-12 Biology* Section 14.4.	❏ Read *CK-12 Biology* Section 14.5.	❏ Read the background and procedure sections for the week's lab.	❏ Do the "Preparing Culture Media" lab on pg. 223 in *Illustrated Guide to Home Biology Experiments*. **OR** ❏ Do the online lab "Land Plants."
Writing	❏ Add the vocabulary to the glossary section of your science notebook.	❏ Answer the assigned questions in the reading section of your science notebook.		❏ Record what you have done in the lab section of your science notebook.
Other Notes				

Week 6	Unit 3 (Survey Course)	2-Day

Weekly Topic

→ This week will wrap up a look at eukaryotes.

	Day 1	Day 2
Textbook	☐ Read *CK-12 Biology* Section 14.4.	☐ Read *CK-12 Biology* Section 14.5.
Writing	☐ Add the vocabulary to the glossary section of your science notebook.	☐ Answer the assigned questions in the reading section of your science notebook.
Events in Science	☐ Choose one of the Events in Science assignments to do and add your work to the events section of your science notebook.	

Other Notes

Week 7 Notes - Plant Evolution and Classification

Textbook Assignments

Reading

📖 *CK-12 Biology* Sections 15.1, 15.2

Written

After you finish reading, answer questions #1-5 in section 15.1 and questions #1-4 in section 15.2. File your work in the reading section of your science notebook. Then, define the following terms in the glossary section of your science notebook:

- ☐ Gametophyte
- ☐ Lignin
- ☐ Rhizoid
- ☐ Sporophyte
- ☐ Bryophyte
- ☐ Phloem
- ☐ Sepal
- ☐ Spermatophyte
- ☐ Tracheophyte
- ☐ Xylem

Experiment - Culturing Bacteria

Purpose

The purpose of this lab is to examine and explore techniques for culturing bacteria.

Pre-Reading

✍ Read the background and procedure sections for the "Culturing Bacteria" lab on pg. 233 in *Illustrated Guide to Home Biology Experiments*.

Procedure

✓ Do the lab entitled "Culturing Bacteria" on pg. 233 in *Illustrated Guide to Home Biology Experiments*.

Lab Notebook

☞ Write down on a sheet of paper or type out your notes as you do the experiment. After you are done, print out your lab notes and add them to the lab section of your science notebook.

Lab Questions

🕯 Complete the review questions of the "Culturing Bacteria" lab on pg. 233 in *Illustrated Guide to Home Biology Experiments*. Record the answers in the lab section of your science notebook.

Online Lab - Seaweed

Purpose

The purpose of this online lab is to learn what it means to be an alga or seaweed.

Pre-Reading

✍ Print and read the section of the workbook for the "Seaweed" online lab.

Procedure
✓ Do the lab entitled "Seaweed" and answer the questions as you work through the online lab.

Lab Notebook
☞ Add the completed workbook pages that were printed to the lab notebook.

Events in Science

Current Events
🕐 Find a current events article relating to the field of botany and complete the article summary sheet found on pg. 246 of the Appendix. Once you are done, add the sheet to the events section of your science notebook.

Historical Figures
🕐 Continue to research the life and work of Carl Linnaeus.

Hands-on Activity

Optional Hands-on
✂ Dissect a flower and identify the various parts. Directions for this project can be found here: http://elementalscience.com/blogs/science-activities/94044099-how-to-dissect-a-flower.

Week 7 Supply List

Weekly Experiment	
Supplies from BK01A Biology Kit	☐ Goggles, Coverslip, Inoculating loop, Microscope slide - flat, Pipettes, Stain: Gram's iodine, Stain: Hucker's crystal violet, Stain: safranin O, Stirring rod, Test tube rack
Additional Supplies From Home	☐ Gloves, Alcohol (ethanol or isopropanol), Alcohol lamp, candle, or butane lighter, Agar Petri dishes (from preceding lab), Agar slant tubes (from preceding lab), Bleach, chlorine laundry, Broth culturing tubes (from preceding lab), Clock or watch with second hand, Large container with lid (for bleach bath), Microscope, Mixed bacteria culture (see introduction), Normal saline tubes (from preceding lab), Paper towels, Tape (transparent, masking, or similar)
Hands-on Activity	
Supplies Needed	☐ Flower, Razor, Magnifying glass, Q-tip, Blank slide, Microscope

Week 7	Unit 3 (Honors Course)	5-Day

Weekly Topic

→ This week will look at plant evolution and classification.

	Day 1	Day 2	Day 3	Day 4	Day 5
Textbook and Experiment	❑ Read *CK-12 Biology* Section 15.1.	❑ Read *CK-12 Biology* Section 15.2.	❑ Read the background and procedure sections for the week's lab.	❑ Do the "Culturing Bacteria" lab on pg. 233 in *Illustrated Guide to Home Biology Experiments*.	❑ Do the optional Hands-on Assignment - Flower Dissection.
Writing	❑ Add the vocabulary to the glossary section of your science notebook.	❑ Answer the assigned questions in the reading section of your science notebook.	❑ Take the Chapter 14 Test from *CK-12 Biology*.	❑ Record what you have done in the lab section of your science notebook.	❑ Complete the lab review questions for the week.
Events in Science	❑ Choose one of the Events in Science assignments to do and add your work to the events section of your science notebook.				

Other Notes

Week 7	Unit 3 (Standard Course)			4-Day
Weekly Topic				
→ This week will look at plant evolution and classification.				
	Day 1	Day 2	Day 3	Day 4
Textbook and Experiment	☐ Read *CK-12 Biology* Section 15.1.	☐ Read *CK-12 Biology* Section 15.2.	☐ Read the background and procedure sections for the week's lab.	☐ Do the "Culturing Bacteria" lab on pg. 233 in *Illustrated Guide to Home Biology Experiments*. **OR** ☐ Do the online lab "Seaweed."
Writing	☐ Add the vocabulary to the glossary section of your science notebook.	☐ Answer the assigned questions in the reading section of your science notebook.	☐ Take the Chapter 14 Test from *CK-12 Biology*.	☐ Record what you have done in the lab section of your science notebook.
Other Notes				

Week 7	Unit 3 (Survey Course)	2-Day

Weekly Topic

→ This week will look at plant evolution and classification.

	Day 1	Day 2
Textbook	☐ Read *CK-12 Biology* Section 15.1.	☐ Read *CK-12 Biology* Section 15.2.
Writing	☐ Add the vocabulary to the glossary section of your science notebook. ☐ Take the Chapter 14 Test from *CK-12 Biology*.	☐ Answer the assigned questions in the reading section of your science notebook.
Events in Science	☐ Choose one of the Events in Science assignments to do and add your work to the events section of your science notebook.	

Other Notes

Week 8 Notes - Plant Biology, part 1

Textbook Assignments

Reading
📖 *CK-12 Biology* Sections 16.1, 16.2

Written
After you finish reading, answer questions #1-4 in section 16.1 and questions #1-5 in section 16.2. File your work in the reading section of your science notebook. Then, define the following terms in the glossary section of your science notebook:

- Cuticle
- Dermal tissue
- Ground tissue
- Meristem
- Mesophyll
- Stomata
- Taproot

Experiment - Investigating Bacterial Antibiotic Sensitivity

Purpose
The purpose of this lab is to investigate and observe the effects of bacterial antibiotic sensitivity.

Pre-Reading
✎ Read the background and procedure sections for the "Investigating Bacterial Antibiotic Sensitivity" lab on pg. 241 in *Illustrated Guide to Home Biology Experiments*.

Procedure
✓ Do the lab entitled "Investigating Bacterial Antibiotic Sensitivity" on pg. 241 in *Illustrated Guide to Home Biology Experiments*.

Lab Notebook
☞ Write down on a sheet of paper or type out your notes as you do the experiment. After you are done, print out your lab notes and add them to the lab section of your science notebook.

Lab Questions
🗲 Complete the review questions of the "Investigating Bacterial Antibiotic Sensitivity" lab on pg. 246 in *Illustrated Guide to Home Biology Experiments*. Record the answers in the lab section of your science notebook.

Online Lab
☞ There is no online lab scheduled for this week.

Events in Science

Current Events

🕐 Find a current events article relating to the field of botany and complete the article summary sheet found on pg. 246 of the Appendix. Once you are done, add the sheet to the events section of your science notebook.

Historical Figures

🕐 Begin to work on your paper on the life and work of Carl Linnaeus. This week, aim to complete your outline and rough draft. See pp. 14-15 for more directions. You will have two weeks to complete this paper.

Hands-on Activity

Optional Hands-on

✂ Sprout an onion by suspending it in a glass of water. Once the roots have appeared, observe the root cap, meristem, and root hairs. If you have a microscope, place a cross-section of the root tip on a slide, stain it, and examine it under the microscope.

Week 8 Supply List

Weekly Experiment	
Supplies from BK01A Biology Kit	❐ Goggles, Beaker - 250 mL, Antibiotic capsule - amoxicillin (250 mg cap), Antibiotic powder - chlortetracycline (3.3%), Antibiotic powder - sulfadimethoxine (88%), Antibiotic solution - neomycin (200 mg/mL), Chromatography paper, Forceps, Petri dishes, Pipettes, Ruler, Spatula, Test tubes, Test tube rack
Additional Supplies From Home	❐ Gloves, Aluminum foil, Balance (optional), Chlorine bleach container, Hole punch (or scissors), Marking pen, Microwave oven, Nutrient agar (see week 6), Nutrient broth tubes (see week 6), Pure cultures (from week 6), Refrigerator, Sanitized work area, Soda bottles, Teaspoon (or measuring spoons), Water - distilled
Hands-on Activity	
Supplies Needed	❐ Onion, Glass, Water, Blank slide, Stain, Microscope

Week 8	Unit 3 (Honors Course)	5-Day

Weekly Topic

→ This week will begin a look at plant biology.

	Day 1	Day 2	Day 3	Day 4	Day 5
Textbook and Experiment	❑ Read *CK-12 Biology* Section 16.1.	❑ Read *CK-12 Biology* Section 16.2.	❑ Read the background and procedure sections for the week's lab.	❑ Do the "Investigating Bacterial Antibiotic Sensitivity" lab on pg. 241 in *Illustrated Guide to Home Biology Experiments*.	❑ Do the optional Hands-on Assignment - Sprout an Onion.
Writing	❑ Add the vocabulary to the glossary section of your science notebook.	❑ Answer the assigned questions in the reading section of your science notebook.	❑ Take the Chapter 15 Test from *CK-12 Biology*.	❑ Record what you have done in the lab section of your science notebook.	❑ Complete the lab review questions for the week.
Events in Science	❑ Choose one of the Events in Science assignments to do and add your work to the events section of your science notebook.				

Other Notes

Week 8	Unit 3 (Standard Course)		4-Day

Weekly Topic

→ This week will begin a look at plant biology.

	Day 1	Day 2	Day 3	Day 4
Textbook and Experiment	☐ Read *CK-12 Biology* Section 16.1.	☐ Read *CK-12 Biology* Section 16.2.	☐ Read the background and procedure sections for the week's lab.	☐ Do the "Investigating Bacterial Antibiotic Sensitivity" lab on pg. 241 in *Illustrated Guide to Home Biology Experiments*.
Writing	☐ Add the vocabulary to the glossary section of your science notebook.	☐ Answer the assigned questions in the reading section of your science notebook.	☐ Take the Chapter 15 Test from *CK-12 Biology*.	☐ Record what you have done in the lab section of your science notebook.

Other Notes

Week 8	Unit 3 (Survey Course)	2-Day

Weekly Topic

→ This week will begin a look at plant biology.

	Day 1	Day 2
Textbook	❏ Read *CK-12 Biology* Section 16.1.	❏ Read *CK-12 Biology* Section 16.2.
Writing	❏ Add the vocabulary to the glossary section of your science notebook. ❏ Take the Chapter 15 Test from *CK-12 Biology*.	❏ Answer the assigned questions in the reading section of your science notebook.
Events in Science	❏ Choose one of the Events in Science assignments to do and add your work to the events section of your science notebook.	

Other Notes

Week 9 Notes - Plant Biology, part 2

Textbook Assignments
Reading
📖 *CK-12 Biology* Sections 16.3, 16.4
Written
After you finish reading, answer questions #1-5 in section 16.3 and questions #1-4,7 in section 16.4. File your work in the reading section of your science notebook. Then, define the following terms in the glossary section of your science notebook:

- ☐ Antheridia
- ☐ Archegonia
- ☐ Sporangium
- ☐ Epiphyte
- ☐ Tropism
- ☐ Xerophyte

Experiment - Investigating Simple Plants: Mosses and Ferns
Purpose
The purpose of this lab is to examine samples of simple plants, such as mosses and ferns.
Pre-Reading
👓 Read the background and procedure sections for the "Investigating Simple Plants: Mosses and Ferns" lab on pg. 271 in *Illustrated Guide to Home Biology Experiments*.
Procedure
✓ Do the lab entitled "Investigating Simple Plants: Mosses and Ferns" on pg. 271 in *Illustrated Guide to Home Biology Experiments*.
Lab Notebook
☞ Write down on a sheet of paper or type out your notes as you do the experiment. After you are done, print out your lab notes and add them to the lab section of your science notebook.
Lab Questions
🦯 Complete the review questions of the "Investigating Simple Plants: Mosses and Ferns" lab on pg. 278 in *Illustrated Guide to Home Biology Experiments*. Record the answers in the lab section of your science notebook.

Online Lab
☞ There is no online lab scheduled for this week.

Events in Science
Current Events
🕘 Find a current events article relating to the field of botany and complete the article summary sheet found on pg. 246 of the Appendix. Once you are done, add the sheet to the events section of your science notebook.

Historical Figures

🕐 Continue to work on your paper on the life and work of Carl Linnaeus. This week, aim to complete your final draft. See pp. 14-15 for more directions.

Hands-on Activity

Optional Hands-on

✂ Make a terrarium so that you can observe the cycle of growth that mosses go through. You will need a large clear jar, aquarium pebbles or other small rocks, a bit of activated charcoal (to prevent bacterial growth), potting soil, and moss. Start by adding the pebbles, followed by the charcoal and soil. Then, place your moss on top of the soil near the edge of the jar and press down gently. Add a bit of water to moisten the soil, put the lid on the jar, and set it in a sunny place. Over the next few weeks observe the moss, looking for the rhizoids and sporophytes to develop.

Week 9 Supply List

Weekly Experiment	
Supplies from BK01A Biology Kit	☐ Goggles, Coverslips, Forceps, Magnifier, Pipettes, Scalpel, Slides - flat, Stain: eosin Y, Stain: methylene blue, Teasing needles
Additional Supplies From Home	☐ Gloves, Microscope, Specimen - fern, Specimen -moss
Hands-on Activity	
Supplies Needed	☐ Large clear jar, Aquarium pebbles or other small rocks, Activated charcoal, Potting soil, Moss

Week 9		Unit 3 (Honors Course)			5-Day

Weekly Topic

➔ This week will wrap up a look at plant biology.

	Day 1	Day 2	Day 3	Day 4	Day 5
Textbook and Experiment	❑ Read *CK-12 Biology* Section 16.3.	❑ Read *CK-12 Biology* Section 16.4.	❑ Read the background and procedure sections for the week's lab.	❑ Do the "Investigating Simple Plants: Mosses and Ferns" lab on pg. 271 in *Illustrated Guide to Home Biology Experiments*.	❑ Do the optional Hands-on Assignment - Terrarium.
Writing	❑ Add the vocabulary to the glossary section of your science notebook.	❑ Answer the assigned questions in the reading section of your science notebook.		❑ Record what you have done in the lab section of your science notebook.	❑ Complete the lab review questions for the week.
Events in Science	❑ Choose one of the Events in Science assignments to do and add your work to the events section of your science notebook.				

Other Notes

Week 9	Unit 3 (Standard Course)		4-Day

Weekly Topic

→ This week will wrap up a look at plant biology.

	Day 1	Day 2	Day 3	Day 4
Textbook and Experiment	☐ Read *CK-12 Biology* Section 16.3.	☐ Read *CK-12 Biology* Section 16.4.	☐ Read the background and procedure sections for the week's lab.	☐ Do the "Investigating Simple Plants: Mosses and Ferns" lab on pg. 271 in *Illustrated Guide to Home Biology Experiments*.
Writing	☐ Add the vocabulary to the glossary section of your science notebook.	☐ Answer the assigned questions in the reading section of your science notebook.		☐ Record what you have done in the lab section of your science notebook.

Other Notes

Week 9	Unit 3 (Survey Course)	2-Day

Weekly Topic

→ This week will wrap up a look at plant biology.

	Day 1	Day 2
Textbook	☐ Read *CK-12 Biology* Section 16.3.	☐ Read *CK-12 Biology* Section 16.4.
Writing	☐ Add the vocabulary to the glossary section of your science notebook.	☐ Answer the assigned questions in the reading section of your science notebook.
Events in Science	☐ Choose one of the Events in Science assignments to do and add your work to the events section of your science notebook.	

Other Notes

Biology for High School

Unit 4 - Animals and the Human Body

Week 1 Notes - Introduction to Animals

Textbook Assignments

Reading
📖 *CK-12 Biology* Sections 17.1, 17.2

Written
After you finish reading, answer questions #1-4 in section 17.1 and questions #1-6 in section 17.2. File your work in the reading section of your science notebook. Then, define the following terms in the glossary section of your science notebook:

- ☐ Amniote
- ☐ Notochord
- ☐ Bilateral symmetry
- ☐ Cephalization
- ☐ Coelom
- ☐ Endoderm
- ☐ Mesoderm
- ☐ Pseudocoelom
- ☐ Radial symmetry
- ☐ Segmentation

Experiment - Investigating Fungi

Purpose
The purpose of this lab is to examine fungi.

Pre-Reading
✍ Read the background and procedure sections for the "Investigating Fungi" lab on pg. 259 in *Illustrated Guide to Home Biology Experiments*.

Procedure
✓ Do the lab entitled "Investigating Fungi" on pg. 259 in *Illustrated Guide to Home Biology Experiments*.

Lab Notebook
☞ Write down on a sheet of paper or type out your notes as you do the experiment. After you are done, print out your lab notes and add them to the lab section of your science notebook.

Lab Questions
🕯 Complete the review questions of the "Investigating Fungi" lab on pg. 268 in *Illustrated Guide to Home Biology Experiments*. Record the answers in the lab section of your science notebook.

Online Lab - What is a Fish?

Purpose
The purpose of this online lab is to explore the evolutionary relationships between a salmon, a shark, and humans, and to figure out what's odd about how we apply the name "fish."

Pre-Reading
  🖋 Print and read the section of the workbook for the "What is a Fish?" online lab.

Procedure
  ✓ Do the lab entitled "What is a Fish?" and answer the questions as you work through the online lab.

Lab Notebook
  ☞ Add the completed workbook pages that were printed to the lab notebook.

Events in Science

Current Events
  🕐 Find a current events article relating to the field of zoology and complete the article summary sheet found on pg. 246 of the Appendix. Once you are done, add the sheet to the events section of your science notebook.

Historical Figures
  🕐 Begin to research the life and work of Charles Henry Turner, who changed the way we think about insects. You will have two weeks to complete your research. After that, you will have two weeks to prepare a two to three page paper on this scientist and his contributions to the field of biology.

Hands-on Activity

Optional Hands-on
  ✂ This week, dissect a starfish using a kit that you can purchase from Carolina Biological, Rainbow Resources, or Home Science Tools.

Week 1 Supply List

Weekly Experiment	
Supplies from BK01A Biology Kit	☐ Goggles, Centrifuge tube - 50 mL, Coverslips, Inoculating loop, Magnifier, Pipettes, Reaction plate - 24-well, Scalpel, Slides - flat, Slides, - deep well, Stain: eosin Y, Stain: Gram's iodine, Stain: methylene blue, Stain: safranin O, Yeast
Additional Supplies From Home	☐ Gloves, Baggies (plastic zip), Bread (without preservatives), Butane lighter (or other flame source), Microscope, Microtome (optional), Mushroom (fresh), Orange slice, Paper towels, Sugar
Hands-on Activity	
Supplies Needed	☐ Starfish dissection kit

Week 1	Unit 4 (Honors Course)			5-Day

Weekly Topic

→ This week will be an introduction to animals.

	Day 1	Day 2	Day 3	Day 4	Day 5
Textbook and Experiment	❑ Read *CK-12 Biology* Section 17.1.	❑ Read *CK-12 Biology* Section 17.2.	❑ Read the background and procedure sections for the week's lab.	❑ Do the "Investigating Fungi" lab on pg. 259 in *Illustrated Guide to Home Biology Experiments.*	❑ Do the optional Hands-on Assignment - Starfish Dissection.
Writing	❑ Add the vocabulary to the glossary section of your science notebook.	❑ Answer the assigned questions in the reading section of your science notebook.	❑ Take the Chapter 16 Test from *CK-12 Biology.*	❑ Record what you have done in the lab section of your science notebook.	❑ Complete the lab review questions for the week.
Events in Science	❑ Choose one of the Events in Science assignments to do and add your work to the events section of your science notebook.				

Other Notes

Week 1	Unit 4 (Standard Course)		4-Day
Weekly Topic			
➔ This week will be an introduction to animals.			

	Day 1	Day 2	Day 3	Day 4
Textbook and Experiment	❒ Read *CK-12 Biology* Section 17.1.	❒ Read *CK-12 Biology* Sections 17.2.	❒ Read the background and procedure sections for the week's lab.	❒ Do the "Investigating Fungi" lab on pg. 259 in *Illustrated Guide to Home Biology Experiments*. **OR** ❒ Do the online lab "What is a Fish?"
Writing	❒ Add the vocabulary to the glossary section of your science notebook.	❒ Answer the assigned questions in the reading section of your science notebook.	❒ Take the Chapter 16 Test from *CK-12 Biology*.	❒ Record what you have done in the lab section of your science notebook.

Other Notes

Week 1	Unit 4 (Survey Course)	2-Day

Weekly Topic

➔ This week will be an introduction to animals.

	Day 1	Day 2
Textbook	❑ Read *CK-12 Biology* Section 17.1.	❑ Read *CK-12 Biology* Sections 17.2.
Writing	❑ Add the vocabulary to the glossary section of your science notebook. ❑ Take the Chapter 16 Test from *CK-12 Biology*.	❑ Answer the assigned questions in the reading section of your science notebook.
Events in Science	❑ Choose one of the Events in Science assignments to do and add your work to the events section of your science notebook.	

Other Notes

Week 2 Notes - Invertebrates

Textbook Assignments
Reading
📖 *CK-12 Biology* Sections 18.1, 18.2, 18.3, 18.4

Written
After you finish reading, answer questions #1-4 in section 18.1, questions #1-4 in section 18.2, questions #1-4 in section 18.3, and questions #1-4 in section 18.4. File your work in the reading section of your science notebook. Then, define the following terms in the glossary section of your science notebook:

- [ ] Cnidarian
- [ ] Medusa
- [ ] Platyhelminthes
- [ ] Sessile
- [ ] Annelida
- [ ] Regeneration
- [ ] Trilobite
- [ ] Chordates
- [ ] Echinoderms
- [ ] Tunicates

Experiment - Full Lab Report
Lab Notebook
☞ This week, choose one of your previous labs and begin to write a full lab report. See pg. 10-12 for directions on how to write a full lab report. You will have three weeks to complete your write-up.

Online Lab - Full Lab Report
Lab Notebook
☞ This week, choose one of your previous labs and begin to write a full lab report. See pg. 10-12 for directions on how to write a full lab report. You will have three weeks to complete your write-up.

Events in Science
Current Events
🕑 Find a current events article relating to the field of zoology and complete the article summary sheet found on pg. 246 of the Appendix. Once you are done, add the sheet to the events section of your science notebook.

Historical Figures
⏲ Continue to research the life and work of Charles Henry Turner.

Hands-on Activity

Optional Hands-on
✂ Create your own worm farm. You can purchase a pre-made one or make your own using the following directions: http://modernfarmer.com/2013/05/how-to-build-a-worm-farm/.

Week 2 Supply List

Weekly Experiment	
Supplies from BK01A Biology Kit	❐ None
Additional Supplies From Home	❐ None
Hands-on Activity	
Supplies Needed	❐ Worm farm kit or Glass jar, Potting soil, Crushed leaves, Worms

Week 2	Unit 4 (Honors Course)			5-Day
Weekly Topic				
→ This week will be a look at invertebrates.				

	Day 1	Day 2	Day 3	Day 4	Day 5
Textbook and Experiment	❑ Read *CK-12 Biology* Sections 18.1 and 18.2.	❑ Read *CK-12 Biology* Sections 18.3 and 18.4.	❑ Read the background and procedure sections for the week's lab.	❑ Begin to work on the full lab report.	❑ Do the optional Hands-on Assignment - Worm Farm.
Writing	❑ Add the vocabulary to the glossary section of your science notebook.	❑ Answer the assigned questions in the reading section of your science notebook.	❑ Take the Chapter 17 Test from *CK-12 Biology*.	❑ Record what you have done in the lab section of your science notebook.	❑ Complete the lab review questions for the week.
Events in Science	❑ Choose one of the Events in Science assignments to do and add your work to the events section of your science notebook.				

Other Notes

Week 2	Unit 4 (Standard Course)		4-Day

Weekly Topic

→ This week will be a look at invertebrates.

	Day 1	Day 2	Day 3	Day 4
Textbook and Experiment	☐ Read *CK-12 Biology* Sections 18.1 and 18.2.	☐ Read *CK-12 Biology* Sections 18.3 and 18.4.	☐ Read the background and procedure sections for the week's lab.	☐ Begin to work on the full lab report.
Writing	☐ Add the vocabulary to the glossary section of your science notebook.	☐ Answer the assigned questions in the reading section of your science notebook.	☐ Take the Chapter 17 Test from *CK-12 Biology*.	☐ Record what you have done in the lab section of your science notebook.

Other Notes

Week 2	Unit 4 (Survey Course)	2-Day

Weekly Topic

→ This week will be a look at invertebrates.

	Day 1	Day 2
Textbook	☐ Read *CK-12 Biology* Sections 18.1 and 18.2.	☐ Read *CK-12 Biology* Sections 18.3 and 18.4.
Writing	☐ Add the vocabulary to the glossary section of your science notebook. ☐ Take the Chapter 17 Test from *CK-12 Biology*.	☐ Answer the assigned questions in the reading section of your science notebook.
Events in Science	☐ Choose one of the Events in Science assignments to do and add your work to the events section of your science notebook.	

Other Notes

Week 3 Notes - Fish to Birds

Textbook Assignments
Reading
📖 *CK-12 Biology* Sections 19.1, 19.2, 19.3, 19.4, 19.5

Written
After you finish reading, answer questions #1-4 in section 19.1, questions #1,3,5 in section 19.2, questions #1,3,5 in section 19.3, questions #1-4 in section 19.4, and questions #1-4 in section 19.5. File your work in the reading section of your science notebook. Then, define the following terms in the glossary section of your science notebook:

- ☐ Ectothermic
- ☐ Endothermic
- ☐ Ovipary
- ☐ Ovovivipary
- ☐ Vivipary
- ☐ Spawning
- ☐ Tetrapod
- ☐ Incubation

Experiment - Full Lab Report
Lab Notebook
☞ This week, continue to work on writing the full lab report you began in week 2. See pg. 10-12 for directions on how to write a full lab report.

Online Lab - Full Lab Report
Lab Notebook
☞ This week, continue to work on writing the full lab report you began in week 2. See pg. 10-12 for directions on how to write a full lab report.

Events in Science
Current Events
🕐 Find a current events article relating to the field of zoology and complete the article summary sheet found on pg. 246 of the Appendix. Once you are done, add the sheet to the events section of your science notebook.

Historical Figures
🕐 Begin to work on your paper on the life and work of Charles Henry Turner. This week, aim to complete your outline and rough draft. See pp. 14-15 for more directions. You will have three weeks to complete this paper.

Hands-on Activity

Optional Hands-on

✂ This week, dissect a perch using a kit that you can purchase from Carolina Biological, Rainbow Resources, or Home Science Tools.

Week 3 Supply List

Weekly Experiment	
Supplies from BK01A Biology Kit	❒ None
Additional Supplies From Home	❒ None
Hands-on Activity	
Supplies Needed	❒ Perch dissection kit

Week 3	Unit 4 (Honors Course)			5-Day
Weekly Topic				
➔ This week will look at fish and birds.				

	Day 1	Day 2	Day 3	Day 4	Day 5
Textbook and Experiment	❏ Read *CK-12 Biology* Sections 19.1 and 19.2.	❏ Read *CK-12 Biology* Sections 19.3 and 19.4.	❏ Read the background and procedure sections for the week's lab.	❏ Work on the full lab report.	❏ Do the optional Hands-on Assignment - Fish Dissection.
Writing	❏ Add the vocabulary to the glossary section of your science notebook.	❏ Answer the assigned questions in the reading section of your science notebook.	❏ Take the Chapter 18 Test from *CK-12 Biology*.	❏ Record what you have done in the lab section of your science notebook.	❏ Complete the lab review questions for the week.
Events in Science	❏ Choose one of the Events in Science assignments to do and add your work to the events section of your science notebook.				

Other Notes

Week 3	Unit 4 (Standard Course)	4-Day

Weekly Topic

→ This week will look at fish and birds.

	Day 1	Day 2	Day 3	Day 4
Textbook and Experiment	☐ Read *CK-12 Biology* Sections 19.1 and 19.2.	☐ Read *CK-12 Biology* Sections 19.3 and 19.4.	☐ Read the background and procedure sections for the week's lab.	☐ Work on the full lab report.
Writing	☐ Add the vocabulary to the glossary section of your science notebook.	☐ Answer the assigned questions in the reading section of your science notebook.	☐ Take the Chapter 18 Test from *CK-12 Biology*.	☐ Record what you have done in the lab section of your science notebook.

Other Notes

Week 3	Unit 4 (Survey Course)	2-Day

Weekly Topic

→ This week will look at fish and birds.

	Day 1	Day 2
Textbook	❏ Read *CK-12 Biology* Sections 19.1 and 19.2.	❏ Read *CK-12 Biology* Sections 19.3 and 19.4.
Writing	❏ Add the vocabulary to the glossary section of your science notebook. ❏ Take the Chapter 18 Test from *CK-12 Biology*.	❏ Answer the assigned questions in the reading section of your science notebook.
Events in Science	❏ Choose one of the Events in Science assignments to do and add your work to the events section of your science notebook.	

Other Notes

Week 4 Notes - Mammals

Textbook Assignments
Reading
📖 *CK-12 Biology* Sections 20.1, 20.2, 20.4

Written
After you finish reading, answer questions #1-4 in section 20.1, questions #1,3,5 in section 20.2, and questions #1-5 in section 20.4. File your work in the reading section of your science notebook. Then, define the following terms in the glossary section of your science notebook:

- ☐ Arboreal
- ☐ Cerebrum
- ☐ Neocortex
- ☐ Placenta
- ☐ Therian mammal
- ☐ Circadian rhythm
- ☐ Ethology
- ☐ Instinct

Experiment - Full Lab Report
Lab Notebook
☞ This week, finish writing the full lab report you began in week 2. See pg. 10-12 for directions on how to write a full lab report. Add your completed write-up to the lab section of your science notebook.

Online Lab - Full Lab Report
Lab Notebook
☞ This week, finish writing the full lab report you began in week 2. See pg. 10-12 for directions on how to write a full lab report. Add your completed write-up to the lab section of your science notebook.

Events in Science
Current Events
🕐 Find a current events article relating to the field of zoology and complete the article summary sheet found on pg. 246 of the Appendix. Once you are done, add the sheet to the events section of your science notebook.

Historical Figures
🕐 Continue to work on your paper on the life and work of Charles Henry Turner. This week, aim to complete your final draft. See pp. 14-15 for more directions.

Hands-on Activity

Optional Hands-on

✂ Observe mammalian behavior. You can do this by observing the behavior of your pet cat or dog, or by heading out to a local park to observe human behavior.

Week 4 Supply List

Weekly Experiment	
Supplies from BK01A Biology Kit	❏ None
Additional Supplies From Home	❏ None
Hands-on Activity	
Supplies Needed	❏ None

Week 4	Unit 4 (Honors Course)			5-Day

Weekly Topic

→ This week will look at mammals.

	Day 1	Day 2	Day 3	Day 4	Day 5
Textbook and Experiment	❏ Read *CK-12 Biology* Sections 20.1 and 20.2.	❏ Read *CK-12 Biology* Section 20.4.	❏ Read the background and procedure sections for the week's lab.	❏ Finish the full lab report.	❏ Do the optional Hands-on Assignment - Fish Dissection.
Writing	❏ Add the vocabulary to the glossary section of your science notebook.	❏ Answer the assigned questions in the reading section of your science notebook.	❏ Take the Chapter 19 Test from *CK-12 Biology*.	❏ Record what you have done in the lab section of your science notebook.	❏ Complete the lab review questions for the week.
Events in Science	❏ Choose one of the Events in Science assignments to do and add your work to the events section of your science notebook.				

Other Notes

Week 4	Unit 4 (Standard Course)			4-Day

Weekly Topic

→ This week will look at mammals.

	Day 1	Day 2	Day 3	Day 4
Textbook and Experiment	❑ Read *CK-12 Biology* Sections 20.1 and 20.2.	❑ Read *CK-12 Biology* Section 20.4.	❑ Read the background and procedure sections for the week's lab.	❑ Finish the full lab report.
Writing	❑ Add the vocabulary to the glossary section of your science notebook.	❑ Answer the assigned questions in the reading section of your science notebook.	❑ Take the Chapter 19 Test from *CK-12 Biology*.	❑ Record what you have done in the lab section of your science notebook.

Other Notes

Week 4	Unit 4 (Survey Course)	2-Day

Weekly Topic

→ This week will look at mammals.

	Day 1	Day 2
Textbook	❑ Read *CK-12 Biology* Sections 20.1 and 20.2.	❑ Read *CK-12 Biology* Section 20.4.
Writing	❑ Add the vocabulary to the glossary section of your science notebook. ❑ Take the Chapter 19 Test from *CK-12 Biology*.	❑ Answer the assigned questions in the reading section of your science notebook.
Events in Science	❑ Choose one of the Events in Science assignments to do and add your work to the events section of your science notebook.	

Other Notes

Week 5 Notes - Introduction to the Human Body

Textbook Assignments

Reading

📖 *CK-12 Biology* Sections 21.1, 21.2, 21.3, 21.4

Written

After you finish reading, answer questions #1-4 in section 20.1, questions #1-4 in section 21.2, questions #1-4 in section 21.3, and questions #1-5 in section 21.4. File your work in the reading section of your science notebook. Then, define the following terms in the glossary section of your science notebook:

- ☐ Connective tissue
- ☐ Epithelial tissue
- ☐ Bone matrix
- ☐ Osteoblast
- ☐ Osteoclast
- ☐ Osteocyte
- ☐ Periosteum
- ☐ Sliding filament theory
- ☐ Melanin
- ☐ Sebaceous gland

Experiment - Investigating Protista

Purpose

The purpose of this lab is to investigate and observe protista.

Pre-Reading

✍ Read the background and procedure sections for the "Investigating Protista" lab on pg. 249 in *Illustrated Guide to Home Biology Experiments*.

Procedure

✓ Do the lab entitled "Investigating Protista" on pg. 249 in *Illustrated Guide to Home Biology Experiments*.

Lab Notebook

☞ Write down on a sheet of paper or type out your notes as you do the experiment. After you are done, print out your lab notes and add them to the lab section of your science notebook.

Lab Questions

🔦 Complete the review questions of the "Investigating Protista" lab on pg. 256 in *Illustrated Guide to Home Biology Experiments*. Record the answers in the lab section of your science notebook.

Online Lab - Bugs and Barnacles

Purpose

The purpose of this online lab is to learn what's misleading about the names we apply to some armored invertebrates.

Pre-Reading
    ∿ Print and read the section of the workbook for the "Bugs and Barnacles" online lab.

Procedure
    ✓ Do the lab entitled "Bugs and Barnacles" and answer the questions as you work through the online lab.

Lab Notebook
    ☞ Add the completed workbook pages that were printed to the lab notebook.

Events in Science

Current Events
    ⊕ Find a current events article relating to the field of anatomy and complete the article summary sheet found on pg. 246 of the Appendix. Once you are done, add the sheet to the events section of your science notebook.

Historical Figures
    ⊕ Begin to research the life and work of James Watson, who along with Francis Crick discovered the structure of DNA. You will have three weeks to complete your research. After that, you will have two weeks to prepare a two to three page paper on this scientist and his contributions to the field of biology.

Hands-on Activity

Optional Hands-on
    ✂ Make a model of the spine using a pool noodle, washers, hair ties, and nylon rope. Directions can be found in the following video: https://www.youtube.com/watch?v=Z6u0xI1JIP8.

Week 5 Supply List

Weekly Experiment	
Supplies from BK01A Biology Kit	☐ Goggles, Coverslips, Magnifier, Methylcellulose, Pipettes, Slides - flat, Slide - deep well, Stain: eosin Y, Stain: Gram's iodine, Stain: methylene blue
Additional Supplies From Home	☐ Gloves, Microscope, Slides - prepared (see text), Specimens - live (see text)
Hands-on Activity	
Supplies Needed	☐ Pool noodle, Washers, Hair ties, Nylon rope

Week 5	Unit 4 (Honors Course)			5-Day

Weekly Topic

➜ This week will look at the human body.

	Day 1	Day 2	Day 3	Day 4	Day 5
Textbook and Experiment	❏ Read *CK-12 Biology* Sections 21.1 and 21.2.	❏ Read *CK-12 Biology* Sections 21.3 and 21.4.	❏ Read the background and procedure sections for the week's lab.	❏ Do the "Investigating Protista" lab on pg. 249 in *Illustrated Guide to Home Biology Experiments*.	❏ Do the optional Hands-on Assignment - Noodle Spine.
Writing	❏ Add the vocabulary to the glossary section of your science notebook.	❏ Answer the assigned questions in the reading section of your science notebook.	❏ Take the Chapter 20 Test from *CK-12 Biology*.	❏ Record what you have done in the lab section of your science notebook.	❏ Complete the lab review questions for the week.
Events in Science	❏ Choose one of the Events in Science assignments to do and add your work to the events section of your science notebook.				

Other Notes

Week 5	Unit 4 (Standard Course)	4-Day

Weekly Topic
➔ This week will look at the human body.

	Day 1	Day 2	Day 3	Day 4
Textbook and Experiment	❏ Read *CK-12 Biology* Sections 21.1 and 21.2.	❏ Read *CK-12 Biology* Sections 21.3 and 21.4.	❏ Read the background and procedure sections for the week's lab.	❏ Do the "Investigating Protista" lab on pg. 249 in *Illustrated Guide to Home Biology Experiments*. **OR** ❏ Do the online lab "Bugs and Barnacles."
Writing	❏ Add the vocabulary to the glossary section of your science notebook.	❏ Answer the assigned questions in the reading section of your science notebook.	❏ Take the Chapter 20 Test from *CK-12 Biology*.	❏ Record what you have done in the lab section of your science notebook.

Other Notes

Week 5	Unit 4 (Survey Course)	2-Day

Weekly Topic

➔ This week will look at the human body.

	Day 1	Day 2
Textbook	❑ Read *CK-12 Biology* Sections 21.1 and 21.2.	❑ Read *CK-12 Biology* Sections 21.3 and 21.4.
Writing	❑ Add the vocabulary to the glossary section of your science notebook. ❑ Take the Chapter 20 Test from *CK-12 Biology*.	❑ Answer the assigned questions in the reading section of your science notebook.
Events in Science	❑ Choose one of the Events in Science assignments to do and add your work to the events section of your science notebook.	

Other Notes

Week 6 Notes - Nervous and Endocrine Systems

Textbook Assignments

Reading

📖 *CK-12 Biology* Sections 22.1, 22.2

Written

After you finish reading, answer questions #1,3,5,7 in section 22.1 and questions #1-4 in section 22.2. File your work in the reading section of your science notebook. Then, define the following terms in the glossary section of your science notebook:

- ☐ Autonomic Nervous System (ANS)
- ☐ Central Nervous System (CNS)
- ☐ Dendrite
- ☐ Interneuron
- ☐ Myelin sheath
- ☐ Neurotransmitter
- ☐ Synapse
- ☐ Target cell

Experiment - Investigating Arthropods

Purpose

The purpose of this lab is to investigate and describe Arthropods.

Pre-Reading

✍ Read the background and procedure sections for the "Investigating Arthropods" lab on pg. 317 in *Illustrated Guide to Home Biology Experiments*.

Procedure

✓ Do the lab entitled "Investigating Arthropods" on pg. 317 in *Illustrated Guide to Home Biology Experiments*.

Lab Notebook

☞ Write down on a sheet of paper or type out your notes as you do the experiment. After you are done, print out your lab notes and add them to the lab section of your science notebook.

Lab Questions

🏷 Complete the review questions of the "Investigating Arthropods" lab on pg. 325 in *Illustrated Guide to Home Biology Experiments*. Record the answers in the lab section of your science notebook.

Online Lab - Centipedes and Millipedes

Purpose

The purpose of this online lab is to learn about what makes a centipede a centipede and a millipede a millipede.

Pre-Reading

✍ Print and read the section of the workbook for the "Centipedes and Millipedes" online lab.

Procedure

✓ Do the lab entitled "Centipedes and Millipedes" and answer the questions as you work through the online lab.

Lab Notebook

☞ Add the completed workbook pages that were printed to the lab notebook.

Events in Science

Current Events

🕐 Find a current events article relating to the field of anatomy and complete the article summary sheet found on pg. 246 of the Appendix. Once you are done, add the sheet to the events section of your science notebook.

Historical Figures

🕐 Continue to research the life and work of James Watson.

Hands-on Activity

Optional Hands-on

✂ Make a model of the a neuron using pom-poms, pipe cleaners, and a straw. Directions can be found in the following video: http://www.sciencecrazy.co.uk/#!Make-a-Model-of-a-Neuron/c1mvs/5556098b0cf298b2d3bd6c56.

Week 6 Supply List

Weekly Experiment	
Supplies from BK01A Biology Kit	☐ Centrifuge tubes (as collection containers), Coverslips, Forceps, Magnifier, Needles, Scalpel, Slides - flat, Slides - deep cavity, Stain: eosin Y, Stain: methylene blue, Thermometer
Additional Supplies From Home	☐ Ethanol 70%, Food for mealworm beetles (see text), Jars (see text), Microscope, Refrigerator, Slides - prepared (Arthropoda), Specimens - assorted arthropods and mealworms, Stereo microscope (optional)
Hands-on Activity	
Supplies Needed	☐ Pom-poms, Pipe cleaners, Straw

Week 6	Unit 4 (Honors Course)	5-Day

Weekly Topic

➔ This week will look at the nervous and endocrine systems.

	Day 1	Day 2	Day 3	Day 4	Day 5
Textbook and Experiment	❑ Read *CK-12 Biology* Section 22.1.	❑ Read *CK-12 Biology* Section 22.2.	❑ Read the background and procedure sections for the week's lab.	❑ Do the "Investigating Arthropods" lab on pg. 317 in *Illustrated Guide to Home Biology Experiments*.	❑ Do the optional Hands-on Assignment - Neuron Model.
Writing	❑ Add the vocabulary to the glossary section of your science notebook.	❑ Answer the assigned questions in the reading section of your science notebook.	❑ Take the Chapter 21 Test from *CK-12 Biology*.	❑ Record what you have done in the lab section of your science notebook.	❑ Complete the lab review questions for the week.
Events in Science	❑ Choose one of the Events in Science assignments to do and add your work to the events section of your science notebook.				

Other Notes

Week 5	Unit 4 (Standard Course)		4-Day

Weekly Topic

→ This week will look at the nervous and endocrine systems.

	Day 1	Day 2	Day 3	Day 4
Textbook and Experiment	❑ Read *CK-12 Biology* Section 22.1.	❑ Read *CK-12 Biology* Section 22.2.	❑ Read the background and procedure sections for the week's lab.	❑ Do the "Investigating Arthropods" lab on pg. 317 in *Illustrated Guide to Home Biology Experiments*. **OR** ❑ Do the online lab "Centipedes and Millipedes."
Writing	❑ Add the vocabulary to the glossary section of your science notebook.	❑ Answer the assigned questions in the reading section of your science notebook.	❑ Take the Chapter 21 Test from *CK-12 Biology*.	❑ Record what you have done in the lab section of your science notebook.

Other Notes

Week 5	Unit 4 (Survey Course)	2-Day

Weekly Topic

→ This week will look at the nervous and endocrine systems.

	Day 1	Day 2
Textbook	❑ Read *CK-12 Biology* Section 22.1.	❑ Read *CK-12 Biology* Section 22.2.
Writing	❑ Add the vocabulary to the glossary section of your science notebook. ❑ Take the Chapter 21 Test from *CK-12 Biology*.	❑ Answer the assigned questions in the reading section of your science notebook.
Events in Science	❑ Choose one of the Events in Science assignments to do and add your work to the events section of your science notebook.	

Other Notes

Week 7 Notes - Circulatory, Respiratory, Digestive, and Excretory Systems

Textbook Assignments
Reading
📖 *CK-12 Biology* Sections 23.1, 23.2, 23.3, 23.4

Written
      After you finish reading, answer questions #1-3 in section 23.1, questions #1-4 in section 23.2, questions #1,3,5,7,9 in section 23.3, and questions #1-3 in section 23.4. File your work in the reading section of your science notebook. Then, define the following terms in the glossary section of your science notebook:

- ☐ Antigen
- ☐ Atherosclerosis
- ☐ Systemic circulation
- ☐ Asthma
- ☐ Emphysema
- ☐ Pneumonia
- ☐ Body mass index (BMI)

- ☐ Chemical digestion
- ☐ Mechanical digestion
- ☐ Macronutrient
- ☐ Micronutrient
- ☐ Peristalsis
- ☐ Dialysis
- ☐ Nephron

Experiment - Investigating Vertebrate Tissue (epithelial)
Purpose
      The purpose of this lab is to investigate and observe vertebrate tissue, specifically epithelial tissue.

Pre-Reading
      ✍ Read the background and procedure sections for the "Investigating Vertebrate Tissue (epithelial)" lab on pg. 331 in *Illustrated Guide to Home Biology Experiments*.

Procedure
      ✓ Do the lab entitled "Investigating Vertebrate Tissue (epithelial)" on pg. 331 in *Illustrated Guide to Home Biology Experiments*.

Lab Notebook
      ☞ Write down on a sheet of paper or type out your notes as you do the experiment. After you are done, print out your lab notes and add them to the lab section of your science notebook.

Lab Questions
      ↯ There are no lab review questions for this week.

Online Lab - Worms
Purpose
      The purpose of this online lab is to learn about worm diversity and about worms that

aren't really worms.

Pre-Reading
     ᷅ Print and read the section of the workbook for the "Worms" online lab.

Procedure
     ✓ Do the lab entitled "Worms" and answer the questions as you work through the online lab.

Lab Notebook
     ☞ Add the completed workbook pages that were printed to the lab notebook.

Events in Science

Current Events
     ⊕ Find a current events article relating to the field of anatomy and complete the article summary sheet found on pg. 246 of the Appendix. Once you are done, add the sheet to the events section of your science notebook.

Historical Figures
     ⊕ Continue to research the life and work of James Watson.

Hands-on Activity

Optional Hands-on
     ✂ This week, dissect a cow's, pig's, or sheep's heart using a kit that you can purchase from Carolina Biological, Rainbow Resources, or Home Science Tools.

Week 7 Supply List

Weekly Experiment	
Supplies from BK01A Biology Kit	❐ None
Additional Supplies From Home	❐ Microscope, Slides, - prepared (Vertebrata) (see text)
Hands-on Activity	
Supplies Needed	❐ Heart dissection kit

Week 7	Unit 4 (Honors Course)			5-Day

Weekly Topic

→ This week will look at the circulatory, respiratory, digestive, and excretory systems.

	Day 1	Day 2	Day 3	Day 4	Day 5
Textbook and Experiment	❑ Read *CK-12 Biology* Sections 23.1 and 23.2.	❑ Read *CK-12 Biology* Sections 23.3 and 23.4.	❑ Read the background and procedure sections for the week's lab.	❑ Do the "Investigating Vertebrate Tissue (epithelial)" lab on pg. 331 in *Illustrated Guide to Home Biology Experiments*.	❑ Do the optional Hands-on Assignment - Heart Dissection.
Writing	❑ Add the vocabulary to the glossary section of your science notebook.	❑ Answer the assigned questions in the reading section of your science notebook.	❑ Take the Chapter 22 Test from *CK-12 Biology*.	❑ Record what you have done in the lab section of your science notebook.	
Events in Science	❑ Choose one of the Events in Science assignments to do and add your work to the events section of your science notebook.				

Other Notes

Week 7	Unit 4 (Standard Course)		4-Day

Weekly Topic

→ This week will look at the circulatory, respiratory, digestive, and excretory systems.

	Day 1	Day 2	Day 3	Day 4
Textbook and Experiment	❏ Read *CK-12 Biology* Sections 23.1 and 23.2.	❏ Read *CK-12 Biology* Sections 23.3 and 23.4.	❏ Read the background and procedure sections for the week's lab.	❏ Do the "Investigating Vertebrate Tissue (epithelial)" lab on pg. 331 in *Illustrated Guide to Home Biology Experiments*. **OR** ❏ Do the online lab "Worms."
Writing	❏ Add the vocabulary to the glossary section of your science notebook.	❏ Answer the assigned questions in the reading section of your science notebook.	❏ Take the Chapter 22 Test from *CK-12 Biology*.	❏ Record what you have done in the lab section of your science notebook.

Other Notes

Week 7	Unit 4 (Survey Course)	2-Day

Weekly Topic

→ This week will look at the circulatory, respiratory, digestive, and excretory systems.

	Day 1	Day 2
Textbook	❏ Read *CK-12 Biology* Sections 23.1 and 23.2.	❏ Read *CK-12 Biology* Sections 23.3 and 23.4.
Writing	❏ Add the vocabulary to the glossary section of your science notebook. ❏ Take the Chapter 22 Test from *CK-12 Biology*.	❏ Answer the assigned questions in the reading section of your science notebook.
Events in Science	❏ Choose one of the Events in Science assignments to do and add your work to the events section of your science notebook.	

Other Notes

Week 8 Notes - Immune System

Textbook Assignments
Reading
📖 *CK-12 Biology* Sections 24.1, 24.2, 24.3, 24.4

Written
After you finish reading, answer questions #1-4 in section 24.1, questions #1-4 in section 24.2, questions #1-4 in section 24.3, and questions #1,3,5 in section 24.4. File your work in the reading section of your science notebook. Then, define the following terms in the glossary section of your science notebook:

- ☐ Leukocyte
- ☐ Phagocytosis
- ☐ Active immunity
- ☐ Antibody
- ☐ Passive immunity
- ☐ T-cell
- ☐ Autoimmune disease
- ☐ Immunodeficiency
- ☐ Carcinogen

Experiment - Investigating Vertebrate Tissue (connective tissue)
Purpose
The purpose of this lab is to investigate and observe vertebrate tissue, specifically connective tissue.

Pre-Reading
∽ Read the background and procedure sections for the "Investigating Vertebrate Tissue (connective tissue)" lab on pg. 336 in *Illustrated Guide to Home Biology Experiments*.

Procedure
✓ Do the lab entitled "Investigating Vertebrate Tissue (connective tissue)" on pg. 336 in *Illustrated Guide to Home Biology Experiments*.

Lab Notebook
☞ Write down on a sheet of paper or type out your notes as you do the experiment. After you are done, print out your lab notes and add them to the lab section of your science notebook.

Lab Questions
🖈 There are no lab review questions for this week.

Online Lab - Tiger DNA Sequencing
Purpose
The purpose of this online lab is to use modern molecular biology lab techniques to determine if parts of a critically endangered species are being traded illegally.

Pre-Reading
∽ Print and read the section of the workbook for the "Tiger DNA Sequencing" online lab.

Procedure
- ✓ Do the lab entitled "Tiger DNA Sequencing" and answer the questions as you work through the online lab.

Lab Notebook
- ☞ Add the completed workbook pages that were printed to the lab notebook.

Events in Science
Current Events
- ⏲ Find a current events article relating to the field of anatomy and complete the article summary sheet found on pg. 246 of the Appendix. Once you are done, add the sheet to the events section of your science notebook.

Historical Figures
- ⏲ Begin to work on your paper on the life and work of James Watson. This week, aim to complete your outline and rough draft. See pp. 14-15 for more directions. You will have three weeks to complete this paper.

Hands-on Activity
Optional Hands-on
- ✂ See how viruses and bacteria spread through touching using several different colors of glitter and a few friends. Have each person choose a color of glitter and rub some on their hands. Then, go around shaking each other's hands and observe what happens.

Week 8 Supply List

Weekly Experiment	
Supplies from BK01A Biology Kit	❏ None
Additional Supplies From Home	❏ Microscope, Slides, - prepared (Vertebrata) (see text)
Hands-on Activity	
Supplies Needed	❏ Glitter, A few friends

Week 8	Unit 4 (Honors Course)	5-Day

Weekly Topic				
→ This week will look at the immune system.				

	Day 1	Day 2	Day 3	Day 4	Day 5
Textbook and Experiment	☐ Read *CK-12 Biology* Sections 24.1 and 24.2.	☐ Read *CK-12 Biology* Sections 24.3 and 24.4.	☐ Read the background and procedure sections for the week's lab.	☐ Do the "Investigating Vertebrate Tissue (connective tissue)" lab on pg. 336 in *Illustrated Guide to Home Biology Experiments*.	☐ Do the optional Hands-on Assignment - Spreading Germs.
Writing	☐ Add the vocabulary to the glossary section of your science notebook.	☐ Answer the assigned questions in the reading section of your science notebook.	☐ Take the Chapter 23 Test from *CK-12 Biology*.	☐ Record what you have done in the lab section of your science notebook.	
Events in Science	☐ Choose one of the Events in Science assignments to do and add your work to the events section of your science notebook.				

Other Notes

Week 8	Unit 4 (Standard Course)		4-Day
Weekly Topic			

➔ This week will look at the immune system.

	Day 1	Day 2	Day 3	Day 4
Textbook and Experiment	❏ Read *CK-12 Biology* Sections 24.1 and 24.2.	❏ Read *CK-12 Biology* Sections 24.3 and 24.4.	❏ Read the background and procedure sections for the week's lab.	❏ Do the "Investigating Vertebrate Tissue (connective tissue)" lab on pg. 336 in *Illustrated Guide to Home Biology Experiments*. **OR** ❏ Do the online lab "Tiger DNA Sequencing."
Writing	❏ Add the vocabulary to the glossary section of your science notebook.	❏ Answer the assigned questions in the reading section of your science notebook.	❏ Take the Chapter 23 Test from *CK-12 Biology*.	❏ Record what you have done in the lab section of your science notebook.
Other Notes			

Week 8	Unit 4 (Survey Course)	2-Day

Weekly Topic

→ This week will look at the immune system.

	Day 1	Day 2
Textbook	❑ Read *CK-12 Biology* Sections 24.1 and 24.2.	❑ Read *CK-12 Biology* Sections 24.3 and 24.4.
Writing	❑ Add the vocabulary to the glossary section of your science notebook. ❑ Take the Chapter 23 Test from *CK-12 Biology*.	❑ Answer the assigned questions in the reading section of your science notebook.
Events in Science	❑ Choose one of the Events in Science assignments to do and add your work to the events section of your science notebook.	

Other Notes

Week 9 Notes - Reproduction

Textbook Assignments
Reading
📖 *CK-12 Biology* Sections 25.1, 25.2, 25,3

Written
After you finish reading, answer questions #1,3,5 in section 25.1, questions #1,3 in section 25.2, and questions #1,3,5 in section 25.3, . File your work in the reading section of your science notebook. Then, define the following terms in the glossary section of your science notebook:

- Luteinizing hormone
- Spermatogenesis
- Oogenesis
- Blastocyst
- Fetus
- Infancy

Experiment - Investigating Vertebrate Tissue (muscle and nervous tissue)
Purpose
The purpose of this lab is to investigate and observe vertebrate tissue, specifically muscle and nervous tissue.

Pre-Reading
Read the background and procedure sections for the "Investigating Vertebrate Tissue (muscle and nervous tissue)" lab on pg. 343 in *Illustrated Guide to Home Biology Experiments*.

Procedure
✓ Do the lab entitled "Investigating Vertebrate Tissue (muscle and nervous tissue)" on pg. 343 in *Illustrated Guide to Home Biology Experiments*.

Lab Notebook
☞ Write down on a sheet of paper or type out your notes as you do the experiment. After you are done, print out your lab notes and add them to the lab section of your science notebook.

Lab Questions
Complete the review questions of the "Investigating Vertebrate Tissue" lab on pg. 344 in *Illustrated Guide to Home Biology Experiments*. Record the answers in the lab section of your science notebook.

Online Lab - DNA Profiling
Purpose
The purpose of this online lab is to use modern molecular forensics techniques to determine which suspect is the likely culprit in a crime.

Pre-Reading
    ↝ Print and read the section of the workbook for the "DNA Profiling" online lab.

Procedure
    ✓ Do the lab entitled "DNA Profiling" and answer the questions as you work through the online lab.

Lab Notebook
    ☞ Add the completed workbook pages that were printed to the lab notebook.

Events in Science

Current Events
    🕐 Find a current events article relating to the field of anatomy and complete the article summary sheet found on pg. 246 of the Appendix. Once you are done, add the sheet to the events section of your science notebook.

Historical Figures
    🕐 Continue to work on your paper on the life and work of James Watson. This week, aim to complete your final draft. See pp. 14-15 for more directions.

Hands-on Activity

Optional Hands-on
    ✂ There is no optional hands-on activity for this week.

Week 9 Supply List

Weekly Experiment	
Supplies from BK01A Biology Kit	☐ None
Additional Supplies From Home	☐ Microscope, Slides, - prepared (Vertebrata) (see text)
Hands-on Activity	
Supplies Needed	☐ None

Week 9	Unit 4 (Honors Course)			5-Day
Weekly Topic				
➜ This week will look at the reproductive system.				
	Day 1	Day 2	Day 3	Day 4	Day 5

	Day 1	Day 2	Day 3	Day 4	Day 5
Textbook and Experiment	❑ Read *CK-12 Biology* Sections 25.1 and 25.2.	❑ Read *CK-12 Biology* Section 25.3.	❑ Read the background and procedure sections for the week's lab.	❑ Do the "Investigating Vertebrate Tissue (muscle and nervous tissue)" lab on pg. 343 in *Illustrated Guide to Home Biology Experiments*.	❑ Do the optional Hands-on Assignment - Heart Dissection.
Writing	❑ Add the vocabulary to the glossary section of your science notebook.	❑ Answer the assigned questions in the reading section of your science notebook.	❑ Take the Chapter 24 Test from *CK-12 Biology*.	❑ Record what you have done in the lab section of your science notebook.	❑ Complete the lab review questions for the week.
Events in Science	❑ Choose one of the Events in Science assignments to do and add your work to the events section of your science notebook.				

Other Notes

Week 9	Unit 4 (Standard Course)		4-Day

Weekly Topic

➔ This week will look at the reproductive system.

	Day 1	Day 2	Day 3	Day 4
Textbook and Experiment	❏ Read *CK-12 Biology* Sections 25.1 and 25.2.	❏ Read *CK-12 Biology* Section 25.3.	❏ Read the background and procedure sections for the week's lab.	❏ Do the "Investigating Vertebrate Tissue (muscle and nervous tissue)" lab on pg. 343 in *Illustrated Guide to Home Biology Experiments.* **OR** ❏ Do the online lab "DNA Profiling ."
Writing	❏ Add the vocabulary to the glossary section of your science notebook.	❏ Answer the assigned questions in the reading section of your science notebook.	❏ Take the Chapter 24 Test from *CK-12 Biology.*	❏ Record what you have done in the lab section of your science notebook.

Other Notes

Week 9	Unit 4 (Survey Course)		2-Day

Weekly Topic

→ This week will look at the reproductive system.

	Day 1	Day 2
Textbook	❏ Read *CK-12 Biology* Sections 25.1 and 25.2.	❏ Read *CK-12 Biology* Section 25.3.
Writing	❏ Add the vocabulary to the glossary section of your science notebook. ❏ Take the Chapter 24 Test from *CK-12 Biology*.	❏ Answer the assigned questions in the reading section of your science notebook.
Events in Science	❏ Choose one of the Events in Science assignments to do and add your work to the events section of your science notebook.	

Other Notes

Biology for
High School
Appendix

Additional Supplies from Home Master Supply List

Unit 1: Cell Structure, Function, and Reproduction

Week	Supplies Needed
1	Gloves, Lamp or book light, Microscope, Scissors, Slide - prepared (bacteria or diatoms), Notebook or copy paper
2	Gloves, Butane lighter (or other flame source), Carrot (raw), Microscope, Microtome (purchased or homemade), Petroleum jelly, Human hair, Pond water, Toothpicks, Vegetable oil (olive or similar), Water, distilled
3	Gloves, Butane lighter (or other flame source), Ethanol 70%, Microscope, Paper towels, Toothpicks, Water, distilled
4	Gloves, Marking pen, Paper towels, Scissors, Water - distilled
5	Gloves, Butane lighter (or other flame source), Butter, Diet sweetener, Fruit juice (unsweetened), Hair dryer (optional), Honey, Isopropanol, Marking pen, Microscope, Microwave oven, Milk (whole), Non-dairy creamer, Onion, Paper bag (brown), Peanut (or cashew, etc.), Potato, Soft drink (Sprite or similar colorless), Sucrose (table sugar), Vegetable oil, Water, distilled
6	Gloves, Blood from uncooked meat, Desk lamp or other strong light source, Egg white, raw, Freezer, Hydrogen peroxide 3%, Isopropanol 99%, Marking pen, Microwave oven, Paper or cloth, black, Paper towels, Starch water, Urine specimen(s), Water - distilled
7	Gloves, Elodea leaf, Microscope, Onion - raw, Prepared slides (see Note), Water, distilled
8	Gloves, Coin with milled edge (optional), Cotton balls, Elodea (water weed; see text), Isopropanol 70%, Leaves, Light source (see text), Meter stick or measuring tape, Microscope, Microwave oven, Saucer, Scissors, Soda straw, Toothpicks (plastic), UV light source (optional), Watch or clock with second hand, Water - distilled
9	Gloves, Balance, Eggs, uncooked (2), Foam cups, Graph paper, calculator, or software, Marking pen, Paper towels, Syrup (corn, maple, pancake, waffle, etc.), Tablespoons, plastic or metal (2), Vinegar - distilled white, Watch or clock with second hand
10	Microscope (oil-immersion if available), Prepared slide: plant mitosis (onion tip), Prepared slide: animal mitosis (optional)

Unit 2: Genetics and Evolution

Week	Supplies Needed
1	*No additional supplies needed.*
2	Gloves, Balance (optional), Beef or pork liver, raw (or yeast), Cheesecloth (or muslin, etc.), Isopropanol (see text), Freezer, Microscope, Paper towels, Saucer, Table salt, Teaspoon, Toothpick, Water - distilled

Week	Supplies Needed
3	Aluminum foil, Batteries - 9V transistor (5, 7, or 9), Gel casting comb materials, Marking pen (Sharpie or similar), Plastic containers, Scissors, Tape (electrical or masking)
4	Measuring spoons, Microwave oven, Soda bottle (2 liter, clean and empty), Sodium chloride (table salt), Sodium bicarbonate (baking soda), Toothpicks, Water
5	Gloves, Balance (optional), Microscope, Microwave oven, Water - distilled
6	Gloves, Bag - brown paper, Camera (optional), Eggshell and yolk, Funnel (or aluminum foil to make your own), Jars - wide-mouth, Mixing bowl or similar container, Newspaper, Pond water/sediment/vegetation, Shredder and/or scissors, Soft drink bottles - 500 mL or 1 L, Trowel, ladle, or other large scoop, Water
7	Gloves, Aquarium microcosms (from preceding lab), Particulate masks N100, Watch or clock with second hand

Unit 3: Ecology, Eukaryotes, and Plant Life

Week	Supplies Needed
1	Gloves, Foam cup, Pond sediment/vegetation, Tablespoon, Water
2	Gloves, Assistant, Camera (optional, with macro feature), Hammer or mallet, Marking pen (for labeling), Field guides to plants and trees (for your region), Plastic bags (specimen containers), Pocket knife, Scissors, Stakes, String or cord (250 feet or 75 meters), Tape measure (50-foot or 15-meter)
3	Gloves, Balance, Chlorine laundry bleach, Foam cups, 16 oz./500 mL, Lamp, fluorescent plant (optional), Paper towel, Pencil, Plastic wrap (Saran or similar), Soft drink bottle - 2-liter, Vermiculite (or other sterile growth medium), Water - distilled
4	Gloves, Saucers or similar containers, Microscope, Petroleum jelly, Plastic wrap (Saran or similar), Spray bottle (optional), Watch or timer
5	Gloves, Desk lamp or other strong light source, Paper towels, Specimens (see text), Water - distilled
6	Gloves, Aluminum foil, Balance (or measuring spoons), Bottle - 500 mL soda, Broth, chicken (or bouillon cube), Cotton balls, Marking pen, Measuring cup -500 mL, Microwave oven, Pressure cooker (optional; see text), Refrigerator, Sodium chloride (table salt), Spray disinfectant (Lysol or similar), Sprayer bottle filled with water, Sucrose (table sugar), Tape, Water - distilled
7	Gloves, Alcohol (ethanol or isopropanol), Alcohol lamp, candle, or butane lighter, Bleach, chlorine laundry, Clock or watch with second hand, Large container with lid (for bleach bath), Microscope, Paper towels, Tape (transparent, masking, or similar)
8	Gloves, Aluminum foil, Balance (optional), Chlorine bleach container, Hole punch (or scissors), Marking pen, Microwave oven, Refrigerator, Sanitized work area, Soda bottles, Teaspoon (or measuring spoons), Water - distilled

Week	Supplies Needed
9	Gloves, Microscope, Specimen - fern, Specimen -moss

Unit 4: Animals and the Human Body

Week	Supplies Needed
1	Gloves, Baggies (plastic zip), Bread (without preservatives), Butane lighter (or other flame source), Microscope, Microtome (optional), Mushroom (fresh), Orange slice, Paper towels, Sugar
2	*No additional supplies needed.*
3	*No additional supplies needed.*
4	*No additional supplies needed.*
5	Gloves, Microscope, Slides - prepared (see text), Specimens - live (see text)
6	Ethanol 70%, Food for mealworm beetles (see text), Jars (see text), Microscope, Refrigerator, Slides - prepared (Arthropoda), Specimens - assorted arthropods and mealworms, Stereo microscope (optional)
7	Microscope, Slides, - prepared (Vertebrata) (see text)
8	*No additional supplies needed.*
9	*No additional supplies needed.*

Hands-on Activities Master Supply List

Unit 1: Cell Structure, Function, and Reproduction

Week	Supplies Needed
1	Microscope, Blank slides, Various materials to examine
2	LEGO bricks
3	Red cabbage juice or pH paper, Common household chemicals such as bleach, ammonia, and vinegar
4	Jell-O, Margarine container, Grape, Other materials for organelles
5	Gummy bears, Glass, Water
6	Leaf, Bowl, Water
7	Bowl, Water, Sugar, Yeast
8	Chicken egg
9	Pipe cleaners, Poster board
10	Pipe cleaners, Poster board

Unit 2: Genetics and Evolution

Week	Supplies Needed
1	LEGOS
2	Easter eggs, M&M's
3	A piece of banana or strawberry, Dish soap, Salt, Ice-cold Isopropyl alcohol (70% or higher), Zipper-style plastic bag, Coffee filter, Funnel, Wooden coffee stirrer, Clear glass
4	Family pictures, Poster board
5	*No supplies needed.*
6	Sheet of paper, Pencil
7	*No supplies needed.*

Unit 3: Ecology, Eukaryotes, and Plant Life

Week	Supplies Needed
1	Sheet of paper, Pencil
2	*No supplies needed.*
3	Sheet of paper, Pencil
4	*No supplies needed.*
5	Gloves, Trowel, Magnifying glass or hand-held microscope
6	Magnifying glass or hand-held microscope, Putty knife
7	Flower, Razor, Magnifying glass, Q-tip, Blank slide, Microscope

8	Onion, Glass, Water, Blank slide, Stain, Microscope
9	Large clear jar, Aquarium pebbles or other small rocks, Activated charcoal, Potting soil, Moss

Unit 4: Animals and the Human Body

Week	Supplies Needed
1	Starfish dissection kit
2	Worm farm kit or Glass jar, Potting soil, Crushed leaves, Worms
3	Perch dissection kit
4	*No supplies needed.*
5	Pool noodle, Washers, Hair ties, Nylon rope
6	Pom-poms, Pipe cleaners, Straw
7	Heart dissection kit
8	Glitter, A few friends
9	*No supplies needed.*

Scientist Biography Report Grading Rubric

Spelling (points x 1)

4 points: No spelling mistakes.

3 points: 1-2 spelling mistakes and not distracting to the reader.

2 points: 3-4 spelling mistakes and somewhat distracting.

1 point: 5 spelling mistakes and somewhat distracting.

0 points: > 5 spelling mistakes and no proofreading obvious.

Points Earned _____

Grammar (points x 1)

4 points: No grammatical mistakes.

3 points: 1-2 grammatical mistakes and not distracting to the reader.

2 points: 3-4 grammatical mistakes and somewhat distracting.

1 point: 5 grammatical mistakes and somewhat distracting.

0 points: > 5 grammatical mistakes and no proofreading obvious.

Points Earned _____

Introduction to the Scientist (points x 2)

4 points: Includes thorough summary of the scientist's biographical information and why the student chose the particular scientist.

3 points: Adequate summary of the scientist's biographical information and why the student chose the particular scientist.

2 points: Inaccurate or incomplete summary of one of the scientist's biographical information and why the student chose the particular scientist.

1 point: Inaccurate or incomplete summary of both of the scientist's biographical information and why the student chose the particular scientist.

0 points: No introduction

Points Earned _____

Description of the Scientist's Education (points x 2)

4 points: Includes thorough summary of the scientist's education.

3 points: Adequate summary of the scientist's education.

2 points: Inaccurate or incomplete summary of one of the scientist's education.

1 point: Inaccurate or incomplete summary of both of the scientist's education.

0 points: No description of the scientist's education.

Points Earned _____

Description of the Scientist's Major Contributions (points x 2)

4 points: Includes thorough summary of the scientist's major contributions.

3 points: Adequate summary of the scientist's major contributions.

2 points: Inaccurate or incomplete summary of the scientist's major contributions.

1 point: Inaccurate and incomplete summary of the scientist's major contributions.

0 points: No description of the scientist's major contributions and interesting facts of their life.

Points Earned _____

Conclusion (points x 2)

4 points: Explanation of why the student feels one should study the scientist and a summary statement about the scientist.

3 points: Adequate explanation of why the student feels one should study the scientist and a summary statement about the scientist.

2 points: Incomplete or incorrect explanation of why the student feels one should study the scientist and a summary statement about the scientist.

1 point: Conclusion does not have an explanation of why the student feels one should study the scientist and a summary statement about the scientist.

0 points: No conclusion.

Points Earned _____

Final Score = (Total Points/40) x 100%

Total Points Earned _____

Final Score _____

Science in the News

Date: _____

Headline: _____

_____

Authored by: _____

My Summary: _____

_____

_____

_____

_____

_____

_____

_____

_____

_____

_____

_____

_____

My Thoughts: _____

_____

_____

_____

_____

_____

_____

Made in the USA
Middletown, DE
09 February 2024